# How To Read Electronic Circuit Diagrams

By Robert M. Brown and Paul Lawrence

TAB BOOKS
BLUE RIDGE SUMMIT, PA. 17214

FIRST EDITION

FIRST PRINTING—MARCH 1970
SECOND PRINTING—NOVEMBER 1971
THIRD PRINTING—AUGUST 1972



Printed in the United States
of America



Hardbound Edition: International Standard Book No: 0-8306-0510-X
Paperbound Edition: International Standard Book No: 0-8306-9510-9

Library of Congress Card Number: 72-105970

# Preface

Circuit diagrams are the basic means for relating information regarding the construction and functions of electronic equipment, a method of showing the circuits and components in symbolic or pictorial form in a universal language. Therefore, the ability to read and understand electronics circuit diagrams is a must for those who aspire to a career in electronics or for those who will pursue electronics as a hobby.

In this book you learn the significance of each type of diagram. Some show specific circuits with each part represented by a schematic symbol——while others use actual photographs or drawings to illustrate the appearance and physical location and relation of each part and circuit wiring—a pictorial or layout diagram. Thus you learn to recognize each diagram for its intended purpose, and develop the ability to derive the correct information from the maze of weird looking symbols and lines.

We begin with the basics—schematic symbols—so as not to leave out anything necessary to a thorough understanding. Then, we progress to actual diagrams and show you how to analyze each type—to read the diagram and acquire an understanding of how the device really works. In so doing, you also learn where to look for trouble and how to determine whether or not a circuit is doing what it was designed to do. The appendix includes all currently used electronic symbols, and a glossary explains the most commonly encountered terms.

Robert M. Brown & Paul Lawrence

# Contents

## CHAPTER 1

# Basic Components

The hundreds of parts that go into making a radio, hi-fi, or television set work are called "circuit components," the resistors, capacitors, tubes, coils, etc., that are necessary to the operation of any electronic circuit. All components are identified by a symbol on the schematic diagram of the equipment, much like the symbols an architect uses to show the stairs, doors, and walls on the floor plan of a home.

The schematic symbol for most components simply tells you what that particular component is. It does not tell you what the electrical characteristics are, just as the symbol an architect uses for stairs does not tell you what kind of wood they are made of. To find the value and ratings of any component, you simply refer to the "parts list." However, some components do have their values either stamped on them or printed in the form of color-coded dots or bands. This is the case with most resistors as well as some capacitors and coils. This color code is standard in electronics in accordance with established Electronics Industries Association (EIA) specifications. An explanation of what this code is and how it works is provided in the Appendix.

There are several ways in which a circuit component can be identified or described: 1) by means of a picture or diagram, 2) by a letter, and 3) by a schematic symbol. Components discussed in this Chapter are identified by their standard letter designation and schematic symbol. Pictures or diagrams of all the many types of capacitors, resistors, etc., would fill volumes and be of little benefit here.

### CAPACITORS

A capacitor is used to "store" electricity. Basically, a capacitor is made of two plates or electrodes which are sepa-

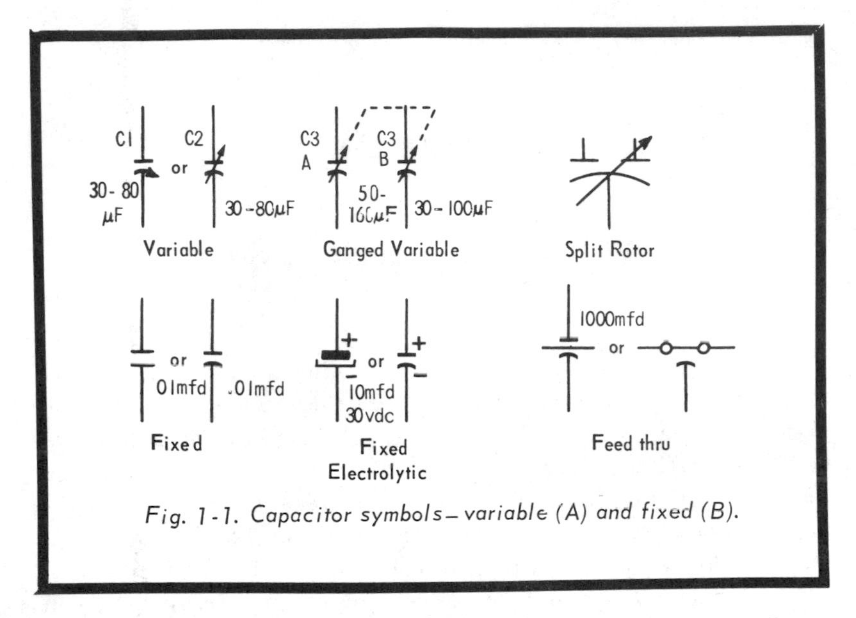


*Fig. 1-1. Capacitor symbols—variable (A) and fixed (B).*

rated by some type of insulation, such as air, mica, glass, or even oil. This insulation is known as the "dielectric" and it is one of the most important inherent properties of the capacitor. Although there are many types of available dielectrics, they can be generally grouped into three classes: air, solid, and electrolytic films. Mica, glass, and oil are examples of a solid dielectric.

Fundamentally, there are two "kinds" of capacitors: those that are "variable" and those that are "fixed." Schematic symbols for both types are shown in Fig. 1-1. On most schematics diagrams the letter "C" is used to designate a capacitor regardless of its type. Neither the schematic symbol or the letter will tell you what the dielectric is made of, or the value of the capacitor. However, this information can often be determined from the capacitor's physical appearance or by referring to the equipment's part list.

There are, though, other numbers and letters marked on the schematic along with the capacitor symbol that do provide some vital information. For example, if you look at a capacitor symbol on a typical schematic, it is generally identified by the letter C followed by a number printed close to the capacitor symbol. To elaborate, let us assume that "C23" is listed next to the capacitor. This reveals that it is, in fact, a capacitor and it is number 23 in the circuit. The reference number is needed to identify the exact component in the parts list. If fact, every component is identified in the parts list with its own reference number.

The value or capacitance of a capacitor is also normally included on the schematic near the component. This may be expressed as simply .01 or .01 mfd. To briefly explain what this means, the letters "mfd" (sometimes shown as uf) stand for microfarads and indicate the electrical size of the component. A microfarad is one-millionth of a farad. If the value were labeled "pfd" (sometimes "uuf" or even "mmf"), it would mean one-millionth of a microfarad. We won't go into the quantity this represents, because for the purposes of this

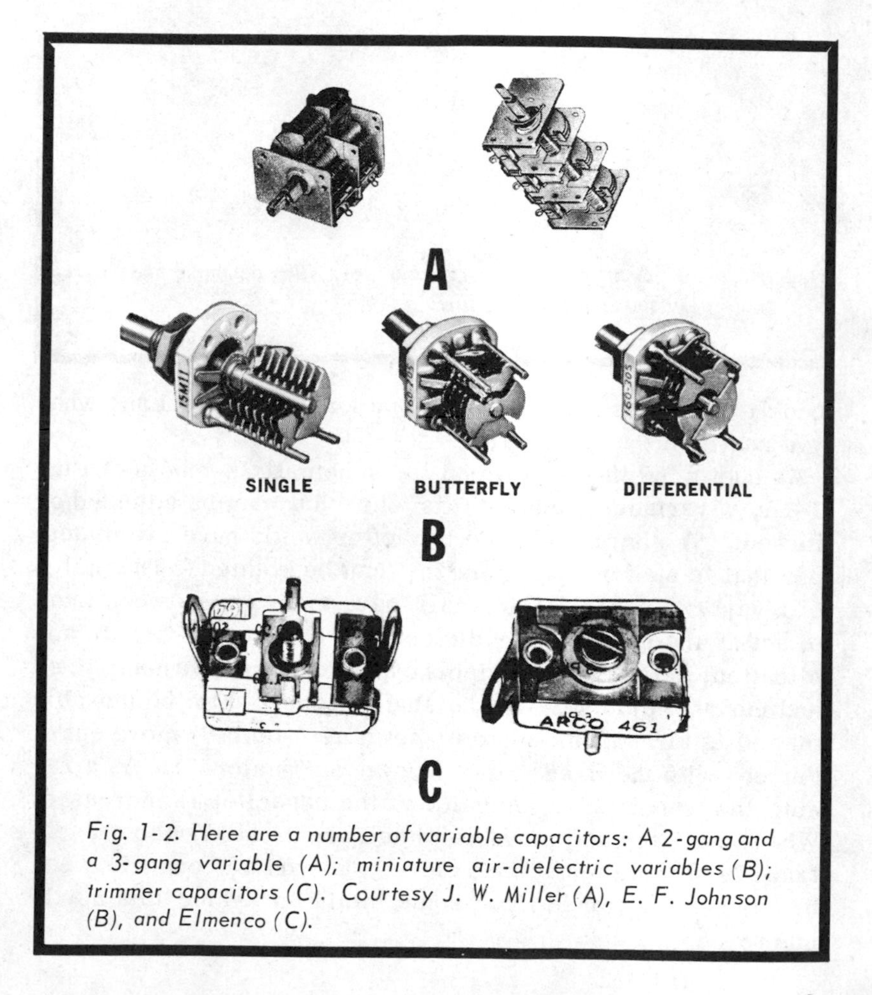


*Fig. 1-2. Here are a number of variable capacitors: A 2-gang and a 3-gang variable (A); miniature air-dielectric variables (B); trimmer capacitors (C). Courtesy J. W. Miller (A), E. F. Johnson (B), and Elmenco (C).*

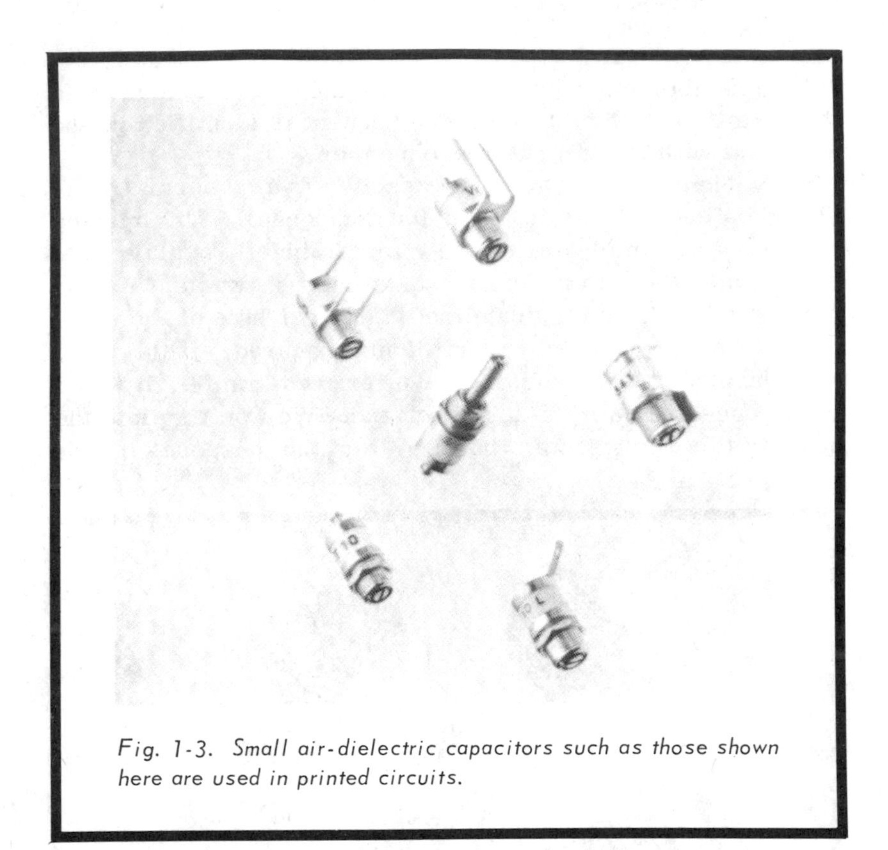

*Fig. 1-3. Small air-dielectric capacitors such as those shown here are used in printed circuits.*

book it is necessary only that you know what it means when you see it on the schematic.

As shown by the arrows on the schematic symbols of Fig. 1-1A, a variable capacitor is one that can be adjusted or turned. A simple variable capacitor would have two plates, one that is stationary and one that can be rotated. The plates of a variable capacitor normally have an air gap between them to act as the insulation or dielectric. See Fig. 1-2A. In application, however, a variable capacitor may have many fixed and movable plates. As the shaft (connected to the movable plates) is turned, the plates (known as "rotors") move out of "mesh" with the fixed plates (known as "stators"). As a result the capacitance or value of the capacitor is increased. When the fixed and movable plates are meshed, the capacitance is at minimum. Therefore, a variable capacitor can be adjusted or varied from some minimum value to a maximum.

For example, the tuning dial of a radio is generally connected indirectly to a variable capacitor, normally by a dial cord, which is in turn connected to the shaft of the capacitor. As you tune the dial of a radio, you are actually changing the capacity in the circuit, which causes a change in frequency. This type of capacitor frequently has two or more entire sections which are electrically separated but mechanically connected to a common tuning shaft. This type of capacitor is known as a "ganged variable." The schematic symbol is shown in Fig. 1-1A and pictured in Fig. 1-2A.

Another type of variable capacitor is called a "trimmer"; some trimmers have an air dielectric while others use a solid dielectric such as mica, glass, or ceramic. Miniature air-dielectric capacitors used for printed-circuit applications are shown in Fig. 1-3.

A "fixed" capacitor, as its name implies, has only one specific value or capacity. They come in hundreds of sizes and shapes with as many types of dielectric materials. Some of the more common fixed capacitors are the disc and tubular types shown in Fig. 1-4, as well as special types such as "feedthrough" and "bathtub" capacitors. Electrolytic capacitors are also fixed, but they are different electrically from other capacitors. Electrolytics use a specific type of dielectric—aluminum foil or tantalum, quite often.

An electrolytic is designed mainly for filtering purposes and it is "polarized," meaning that one terminal of the capacitor is positive with respect to the other, just like a magnet. The polarized terminals on an electrolytic are identified by positive (-) and negative (+) signs stamped right on the component, which also helps to identify the fact that it is an electrolytic capacitor. Most schematics identify an electrolytic by placing the plus and minus signs on the schematic next to the symbol, which also indicates the circuit polarity connections for the capacitor. Another type of electrolytic capacitor is the "non-polarized" unit. However, these are marked in the same manner and used in special circuit applications.

## RESISTORS

Resistors, like capacitors, are found in almost every type of electronic circuit. Resistors are devices used to restrict

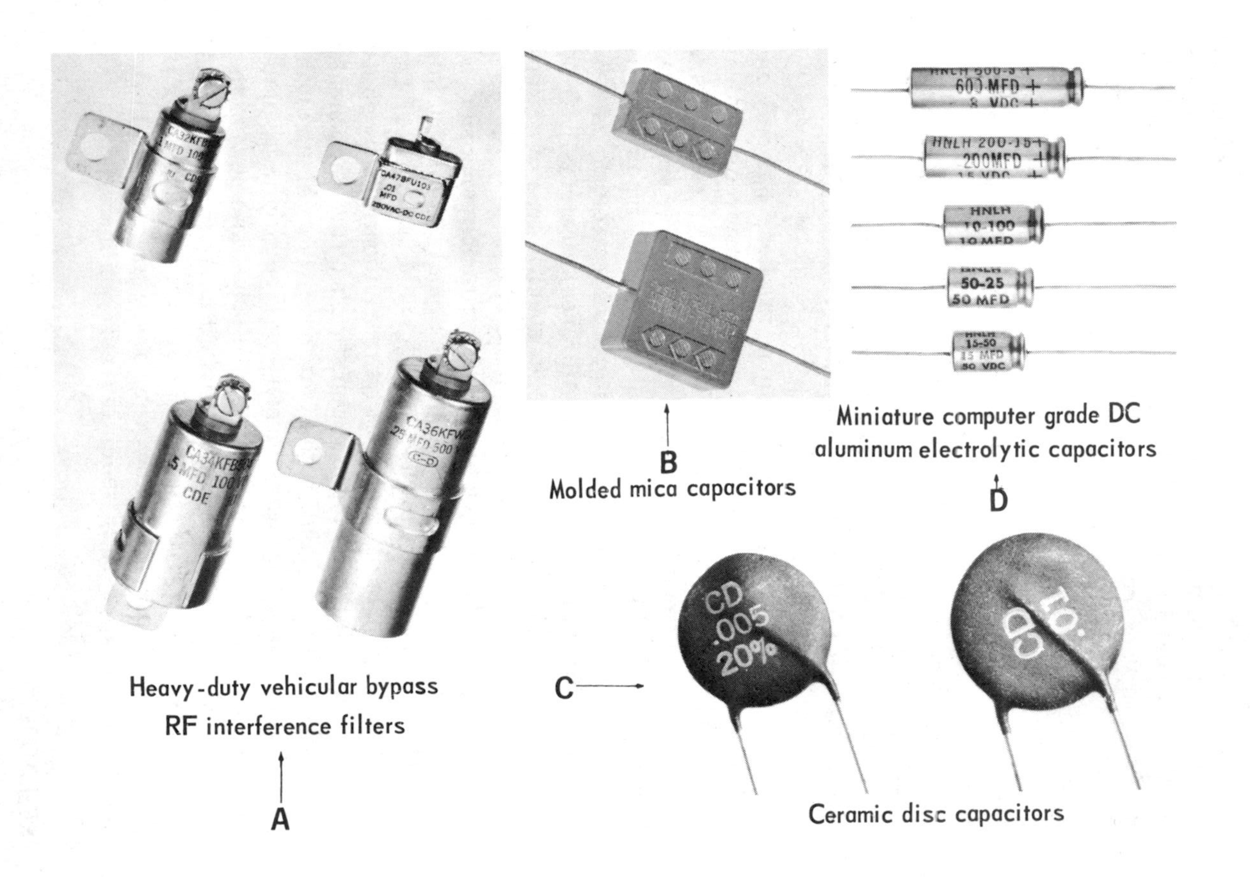


Heavy-duty vehicular bypass
RF interference filters

A

B
Molded mica capacitors

Miniature computer grade DC
aluminum electrolytic capacitors

D

C

Ceramic disc capacitors

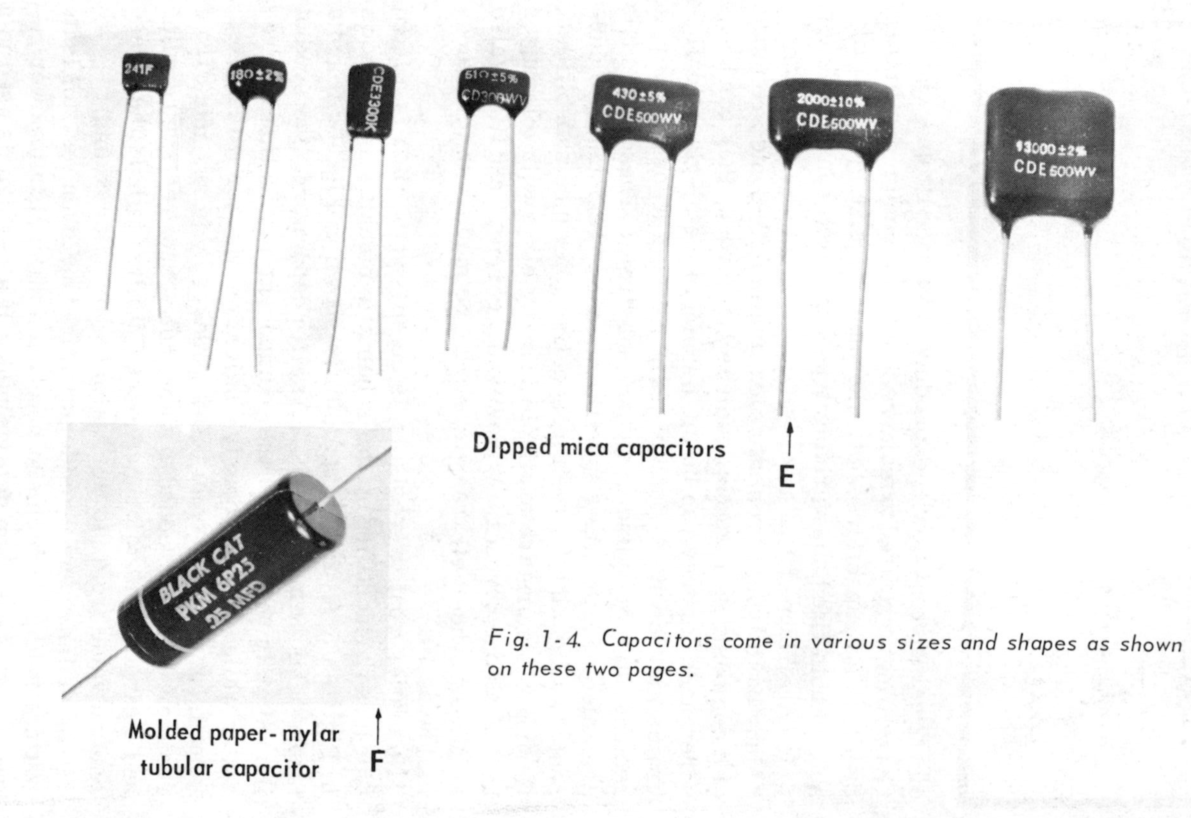


*Fig. 1-4. Capacitors come in various sizes and shapes as shown on these two pages.*

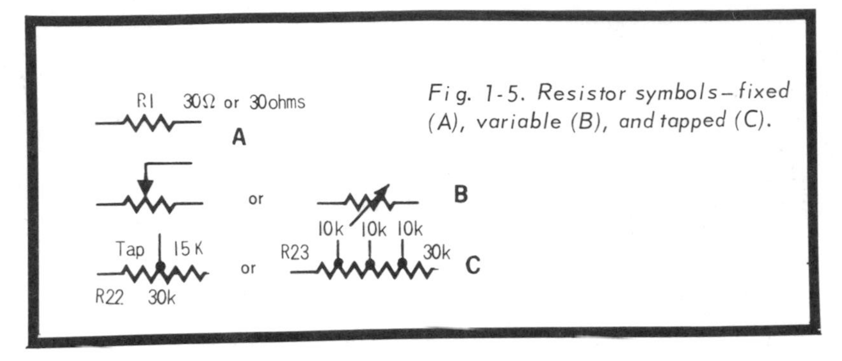


*Fig. 1-5. Resistor symbols—fixed (A), variable (B), and tapped (C).*

electrical current flow and produce a voltage drop. The variety of material used to make resistors is much more limited than it is for capacitors, but, like capacitors, they are available in both fixed and variable types and even some varieties which are "tapped."

Many basic types of resistors are available. Some are made of a composition material such as 1). carbon; they can be 2). wirewound, or they can be 3). cermet (a metal-glaze configuration) made with 4). metal film, vacuum deposited over a rectangular- or cylinder-shaped substrate. These materials are selected to provide a specific amount of resistance to current flow and also for their respective tolerance capabilities. Carbon resistors are available in many sizes with tolerances as low as one percent. Wirewound, cermet, and film (also known as Film-met) resistors can be made with tolerances as low as .01%.

No matter what a resistor is composed of, if it is a fixed type it can be identified by the schematic circuit symbol shown in Fig. 1-5A. A variable resistor is shown in Fig. 1-5B and a tapped resistor in Fig. 1-5C. As with capacitors, the symbol immediately reveals that the component in question is a resistor while simultaneously indicating whether it is a fixed, tapped, or variable type. But unlike capacitors, most fixed resistors are colorcoded to show their exact resistance value and their inherent tolerance—the "ability" to hold their designated value (refer to the Appendix for color coding).

Another important consideration for any given resistor is its wattage rating, which can be chosen after circuit power requirements have been determined. If a resistor is used in a circuit where heavy current is flowing and its resistance value causes a large voltage drop, the resistor must be able to safely dissipate the resulting degree of heat that will be generated. Therefore, resistors are also rated by the amount of heat (watts) they can safely withstand. Physically, the larger the resistor, the more heat it can dissipate. Which means that you can generally judge the wattage rating of many resistors simply by looking at them.

As indicated earlier, all components have a schematic reference letter number, and for resistors it is the letter "R." Suppose you see R23 printed next to a resistor symbol. This means it is a resistor and the twenty-third one on the schematic. Again, you need this reference number to identify the component in the parts list. Resistor values also are printed near the symbol on most schematics.

The value or quantity of resistance is measured in terms of "ohms." This term is given the Greek symbol Omega or Ω So when you see 100Ω next to a resistor, you know its value is 100 ohms. Resistor values range from fractions of an ohm into the thousands and millions of ohms. It would be ridiculous to try to print that many numbers on a schematic, so letters were adopted which represent one thousand and one million—the letter "K," meaning "kilo" or one thousand, the letter "M," meaning mega or one million. Therefore, a 10,000-ohm resistor would be labeled 10K on a schematic while a 10-million ohm resistor would be labeled 10M or 10 Meg. The symbol (Ω) for ohms is left off the schematic because it is assumed anyway.

Several types of resistors are shown in Fig. 1-6A. A fixed resistor is a specific value in ohms. A tapped or adjustable resistor is a kind of semi-fixed resistor, usually wirewound with one or more slider arms which are adjusted to a point along the length of the resistor to provide only a certain amount of total resistance. The tap is then tightened and left at this point. A tapped resistor differs from a variable resistor in that it is normally not changed in value once it is adjusted. Fig. 1-7 shows how a fixed wirewound resistor is made.

A variable resistor, sometimes called a rheostat, potentiometer, or just plain "pot," can be rotated or adjusted from zero to its full value as the operator desires. The volume control on your radio, hi-fi, and TV set are all examples of variable resistors or pots. See Fig. 1-8. Transistorized equipments often use miniaturized versions of variable re-

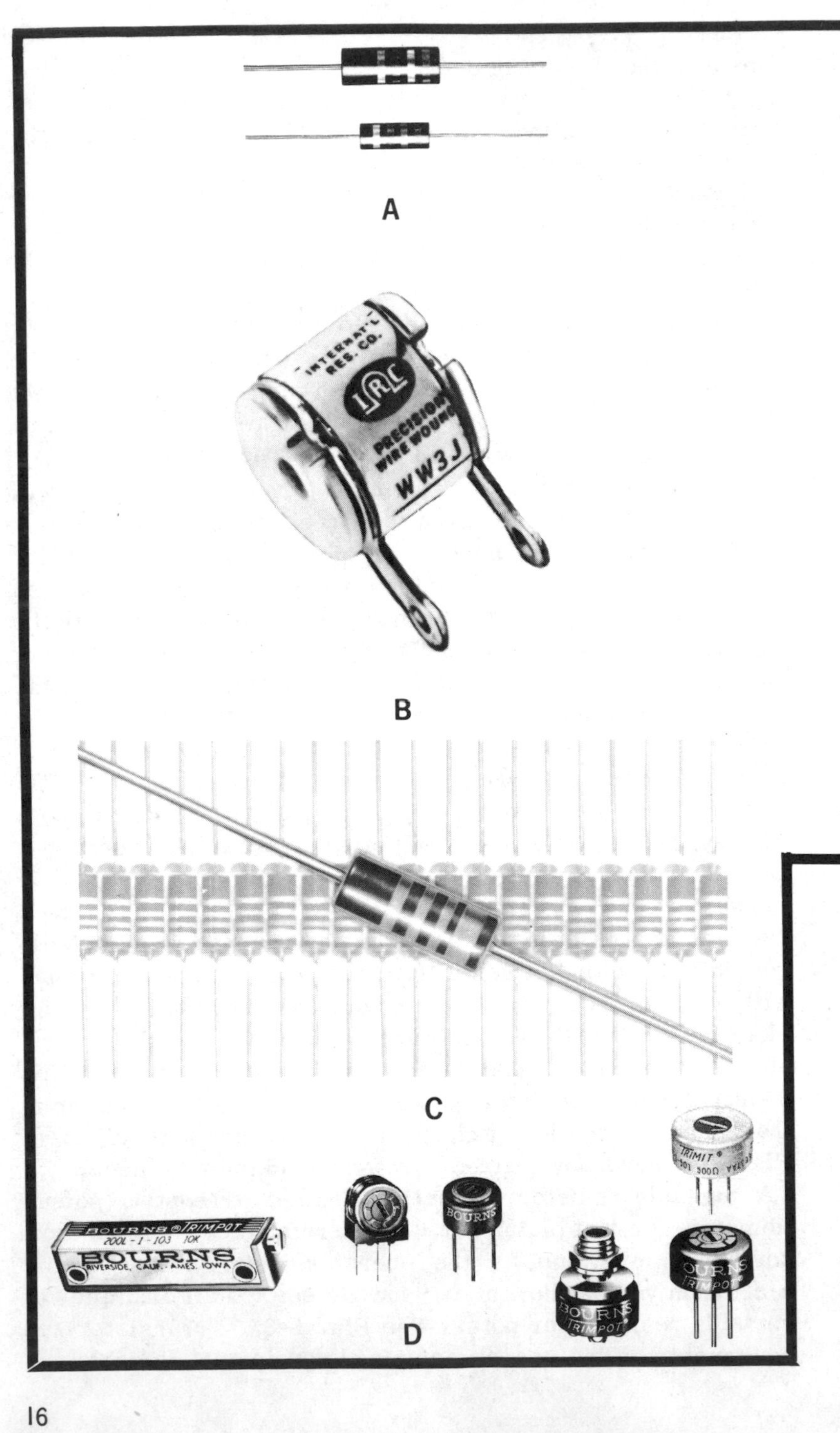
A
INTERNAT'L RES. CO.
IRC
PRECISION WIRE WOUND
WW3J
B
C
BOURNS ®TRIMPOT
200L-1-103 10K
BOURNS
RIVERSIDE, CALIF. - AMES, IOWA
BOURNS
TRIMIT
BOURNS TRIMPOT
BOURNS TRIMPOT
D

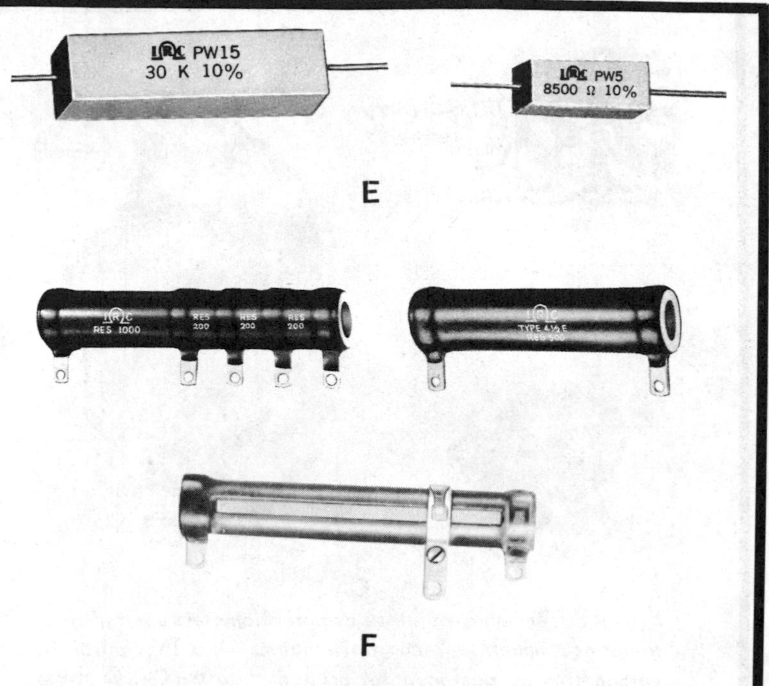


*Fig. 1-6. Like capacitors, resistors are also made in a variety of sizes: composition carbon fixed (A); precusion wirewound fixed (B); molded wirewound (C); variable ''trimpots'' used in printed circuits (D); small fixed power (E) and wirewound power resistors (F) Courtesy IRC (A, B, C, E, F) and Burns (D).*

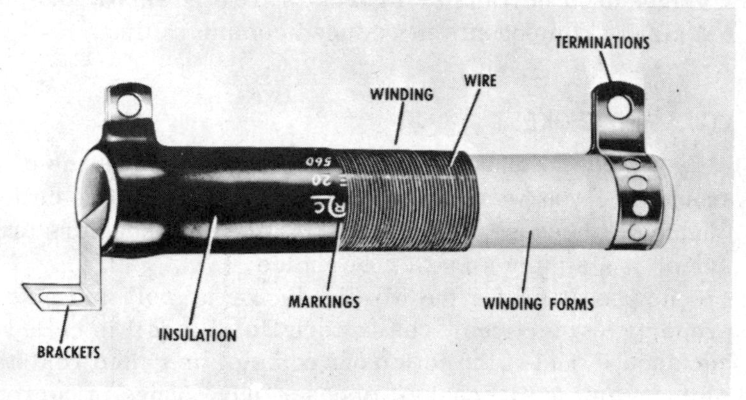


*Fig. 1-7. Construction details of a wirewound power resistor. Courtesy IRC.*

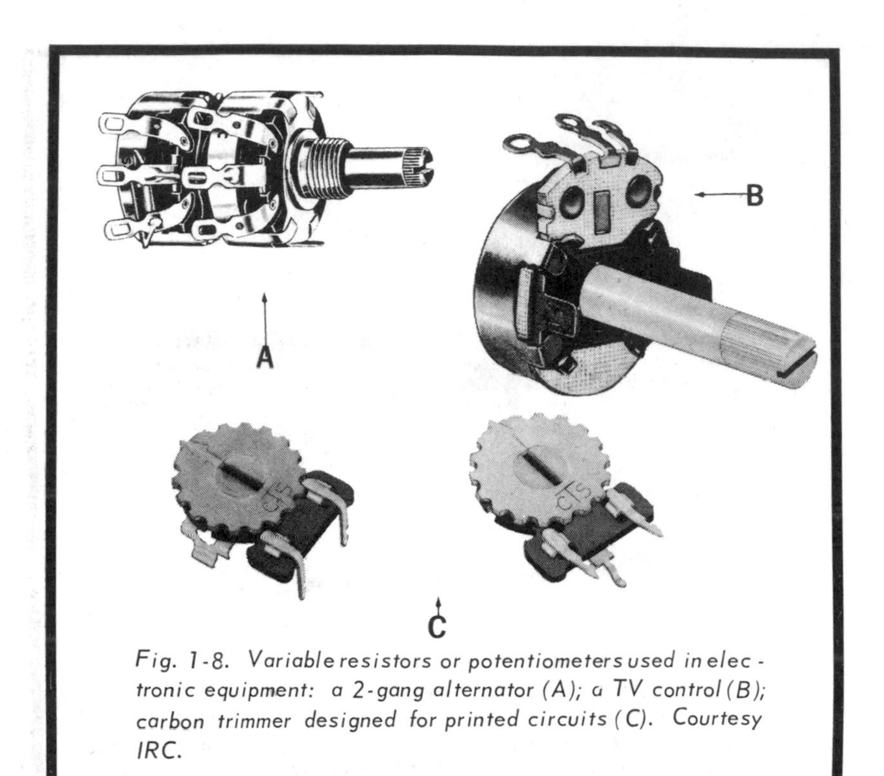


*Fig. 1-8. Variable resistors or potentiometers used in electronic equipment: a 2-gang alternator (A); a TV control (B); carbon trimmer designed for printed circuits (C). Courtesy IRC.*

sistors called "trim pots." With the trend toward more miniaturization in all types of circuits, resistors (as well as other components) get smaller and smaller. Since the currents and voltages used in transistor circuits are also small, the physical size of components in reduced considerably.

## COILS AND CHOKES

If you were to take a pencil and wrap several turns of wire around it, you would have a coil. It could also be called an "inductor" because, basically, coils and inductors are the same; it's simply a matter of choice.

Some people prefer the word inductor to coil because the property or electrical characteristic of a coil is called "inductance," just as the action of a resistor is called resistance. An inductor (coil, choke) opposes any change in current by inducing an opposing voltage. Coils (or inductors) and chokes are the same in this respect. Coils are designated by the letter "L" and the term used to indicate the amount of inductance is the "henry." (See Fig. 1-9)

A coil or choke in radio circuits usually has a value less than one henry so the terms "milli" or "micro" (abbreviated mh or uh) are used. For example, next to a coil or choke on the schematic you will likely have the reference number, let's say it's L12, and the value: 10mh. L12 means it is the 12th inductor and 10mh means that it has a value of 10 thousandths of a henry. The micro symbol (u) means the same as in the case of the capacitors—one millionth. In this case, a 10 uh coil would be read as 10 microhenrys. Illustrated in Fig. 1-10 are various types of coils and in Fig. 1-11 several commonly used chokes.

In actual circuit applications, the amount of inductance of a coil or choke depends on many things, such as the number of turns of wire, the size of the wire, the size of the form, and the type of core. As suggested earlier, if you wound a coil of wire on a pencil, you would have an inductor with a certain amount of distortion. If you were to wind the same coil on an iron rod, the inductance would be much greater. Also, if you wound the coil on a form and placed an iron slug inside the form which could be moved into or out of the coil, you would have a coil with a variable inductance. Chokes are not variable.

## TRANSFORMERS

Transformers differ from coils in that they are a combination of two or more coils positioned close to each other, physi-

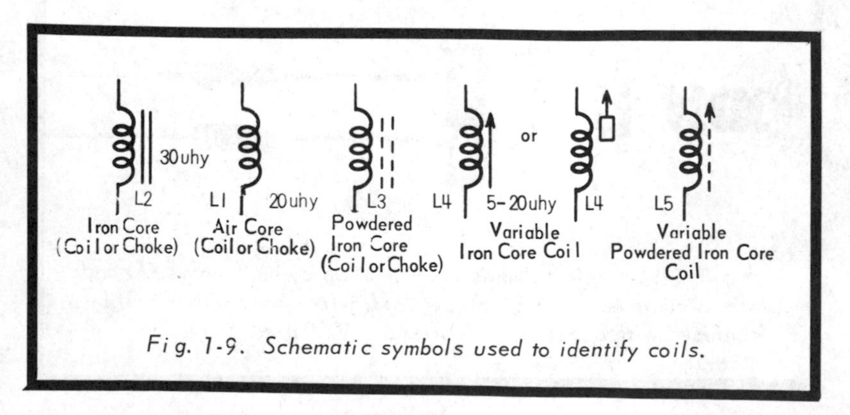


*Fig. 1-9. Schematic symbols used to identify coils.*

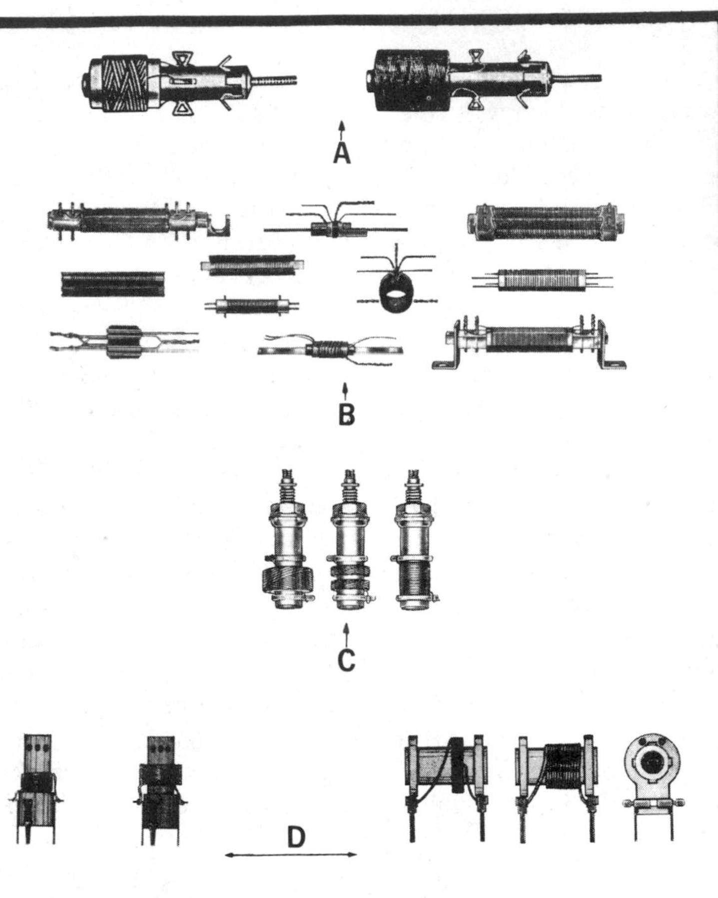


*Fig. 1-10. These are some of the most popular variable coils you'll encounter: adjustable coils for TV sets (A); antenna-matching or balun (B); RF coils (C); and coils designed for mounting on printed-circuit boards. Courtesy J. W. Miller.*

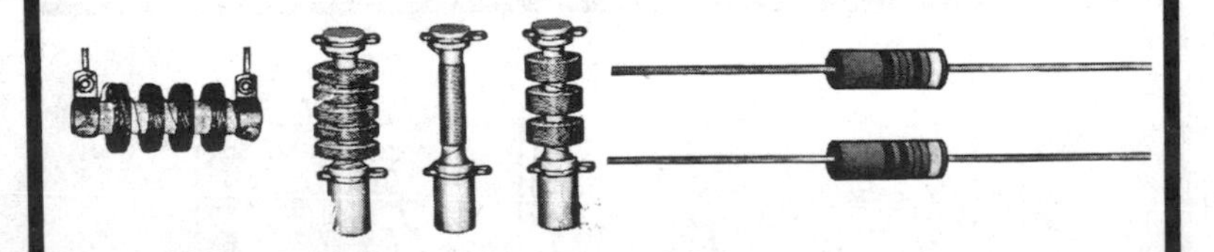

*Fig. 1-11. Some RF chokes are wound on ceramic cores (A) and others contained within molded plastic-like body which can be confused with a resistor. Courtesy J. W. Miller.*

cally, which provides the means to transfer energy from one coil to another. As shown in Fig. 1-12, the two coils of a transformer are labeled "primary" and "secondary." Just as in the case of coils or inductors, a transformer can have an air core, a fixed iron core, or an adjustable iron core. When an AC signal is connected across the primary coil, the resulting magnetic field causes or "induces" a voltage in the secondary winding and so the signal is transfered.

Many things actually take place during this transfer, but as a matter of information, the signal appearing at the secondary will not be exactly like the signal coming into the primary because of losses in the transformer windings, the number of turns, etc.

Transformers are labeled with the letter "T" on a schematic diagram. But unlike capacitors, resistors, and coils, their values are not normally given, except perhaps in the parts list. Since transformers have inductance just as coils, the primary and secondary coil windings will have some value in

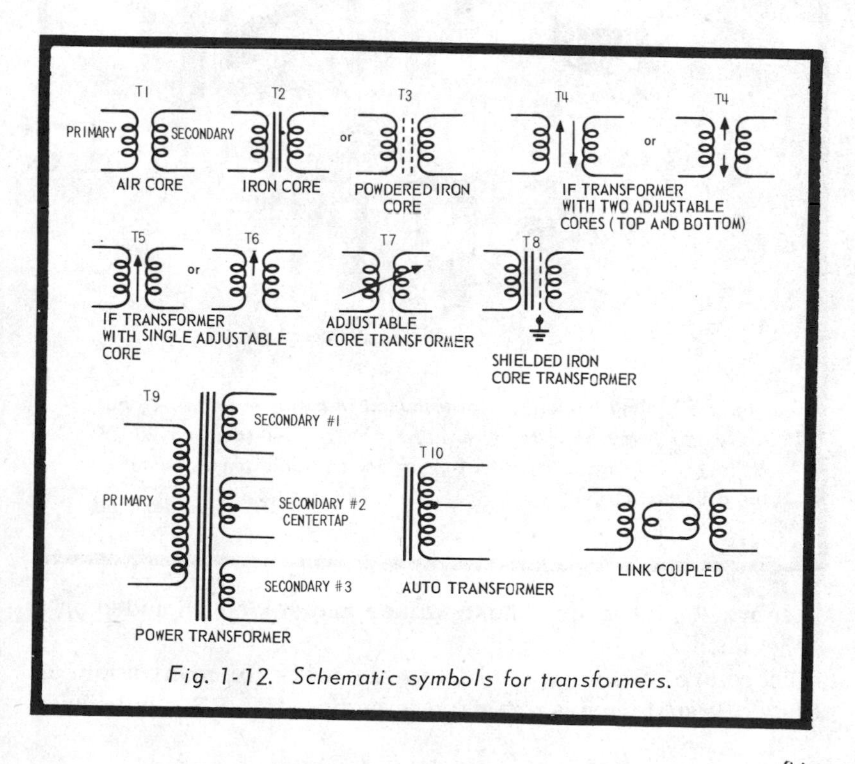

*Fig. 1-12. Schematic symbols for transformers.*

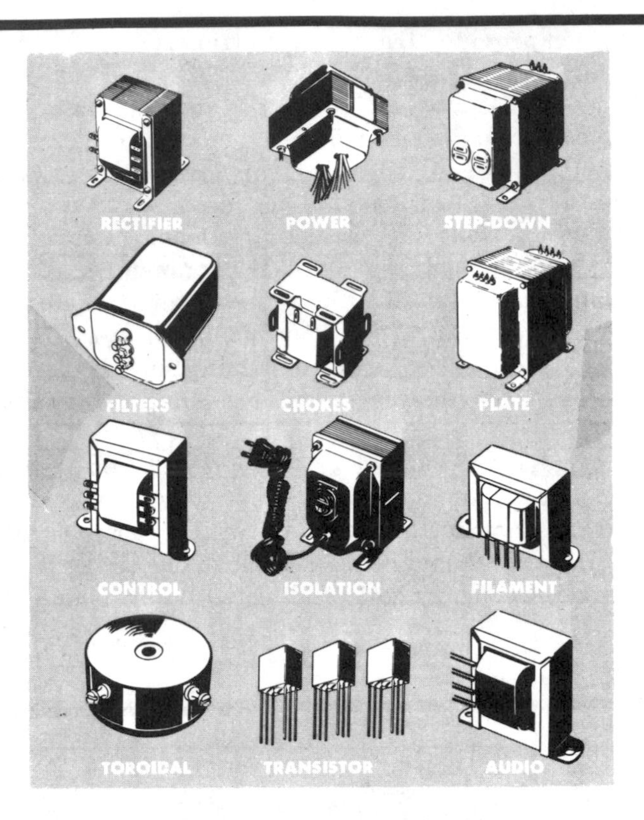

*Fig. 1-13. IF transformers are housed in metal shields (A), partially cut away here to reveal the actual coil (courtesy J. W. Miller). At B are sketches of a variety of transformers manufactured by Stancor.*

"henrys." However, these values are seldom included on a schematic.

There are many types of transformers for many applications. Transformers are used in audio, IF, RF, and power supply circuits. Transformers designed for audio and power supply circuits generally have color-coded leads indicating primary and secondary windings. Like the resistor and capacitor color codes, transformer coding is standardized by the EIA and it appears in the Appendix. Some of the more common types of transformers are shown in Fig. 1-13.

## BATTERIES

No doubt you have used many kinds of batteries in your everyday activities. Your automobile, transistor radio, and flashlight all operate from batteries. It is a source of power in the form of a DC voltage which comes from "cells" that change chemical energy into electrical energy.

Batteries are classified as being either "primary" or "secondary" and they can by either "wet" or "dry." The batteries in your flashlight are examples of dry primary cells, so are the batteries in your transistor radio. Primary batteries are made to develop a certain amount of energy and when that energy is used up, you install new batteries. Your automobile battery is a secondary coil—a lead-acid wet cell—and it can be recharged with energy so it will last for years.

All batteries are represented by the same schematic symbol. Fig. 1-14 shows a single-cell battery and a multi-cell battery, which is nothing more than a group of single cells connected in series. The symbol does not show the type of battery, but for practical purposes it is not important. The voltage and polarity shown are important, however.

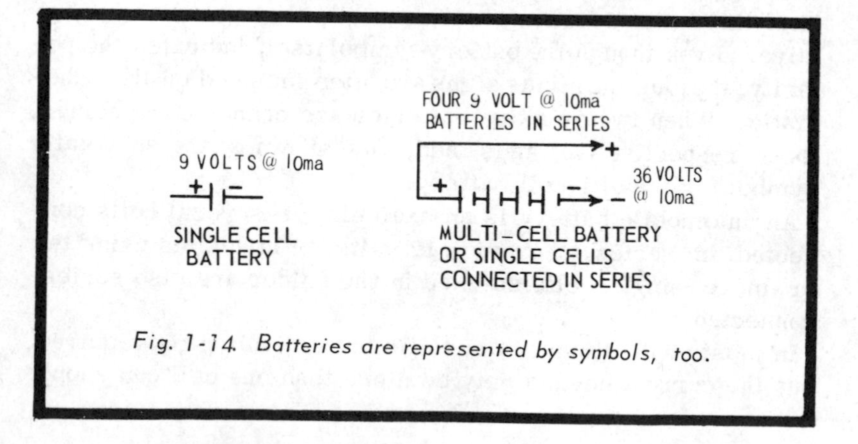


*Fig. 1-14. Batteries are represented by symbols, too.*

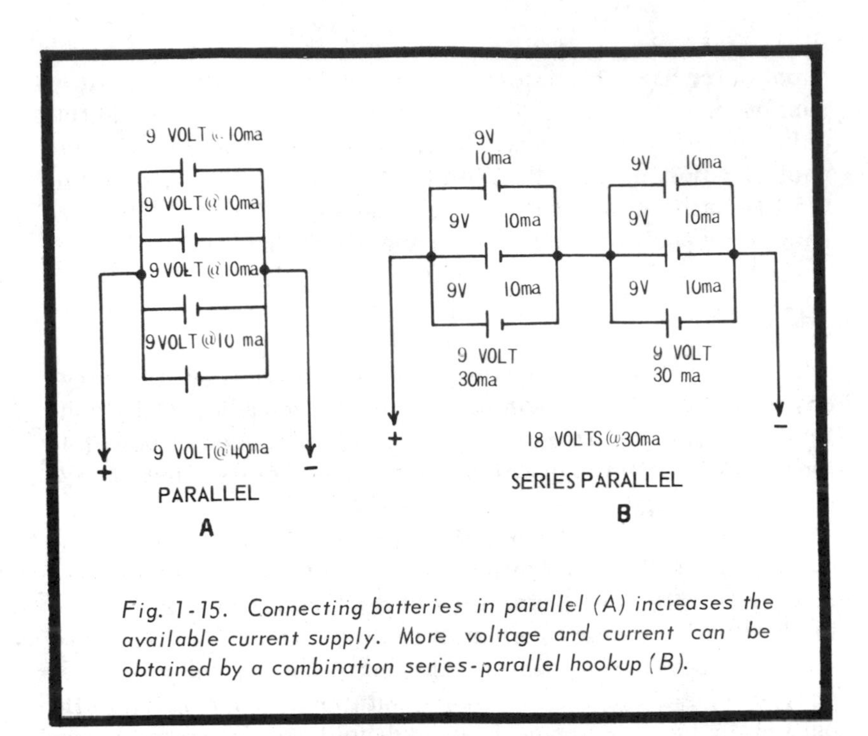


*Fig. 1-15. Connecting batteries in parallel (A) increases the available current supply. More voltage and current can be obtained by a combination series-parallel hookup (B).*

If your radio schematic or instructions call for a 9-volt battery, you wouldn't install one that is 22 volts, and you surely wouldn't get much music out of the radio if you used a 1.5-volt flashlight battery instead of a 9-volt battery. No matter what you use a battery for, it must be installed with the right polarity or it will not work.

Batteries have two poles or terminals—one positive (+) and one negative (–). As illustrated in Fig. 1-14, the longer vertical line is the positive terminal while the short line is negative. Even though the battery symbol itself indicates the polarity, the plus and minus signs are often included on the schematic. When two or more batteries are connected in series, their respective voltages add, as shown by the schematic symbol for a multi-cell battery.

An automobile battery is an example of several cells connected in series to provide 12 volts. Flashlights using two or more single cells stacked in the holder are also series-connected.

In most applications, a specific battery voltage is required, but the current needed may be more than one cell can supply without putting an excessive drain on it. In this application, batteries can be connected in parallel as shown in Fig. 1-15A. This arrangement provides the same voltage as one battery, but now their respective current capabilities are added. When using this type of connection, the batteries should all be the same voltage rating to prevent excessive current drain on the battery having a lower voltage. Batteries can also be connected in series and parallel combinations to provide both more voltage and current as shown in Fig. 1-15B.

As mentioned previously, the schematic symbol does not tell us what kind of battery it is. But certain batteries are used in given applications primarily because of their ratings, size, and cost. Fig. 1-16 shows several types. For example, you could use an automobile battery to operate a flashlight or a transistor radio, but you would have a pretty tough time carrying it around. Moreover, a flashlight or transistor radio doesn't need the current available from an automobile battery—a small dry cell works just as well and lasts long enough to make the cost of replacing these cells periodically a rela-

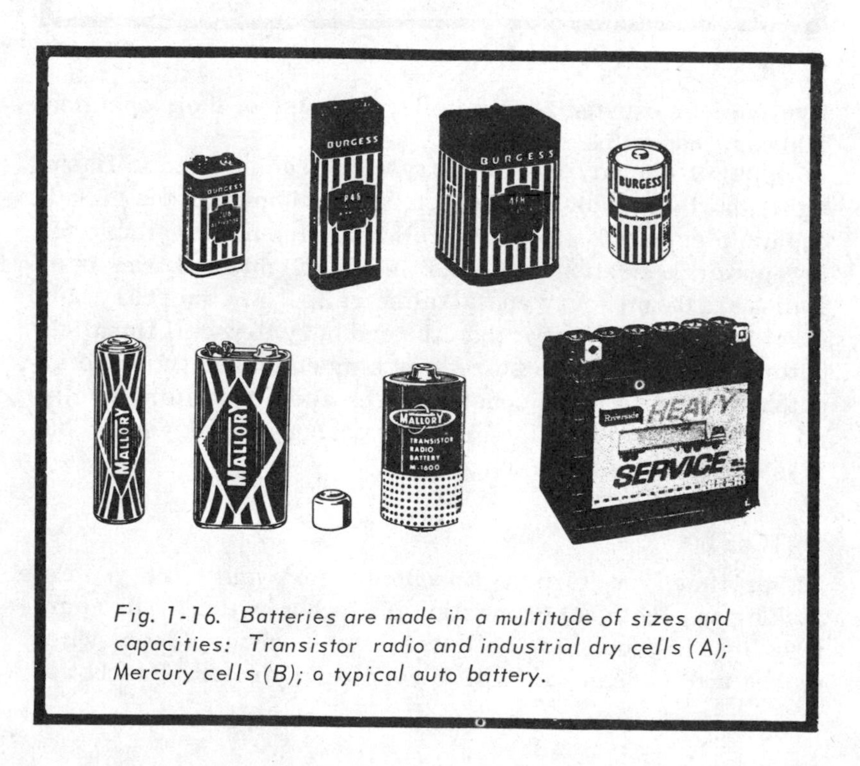


*Fig. 1-16. Batteries are made in a multitude of sizes and capacities: Transistor radio and industrial dry cells (A); Mercury cells (B); a typical auto battery.*

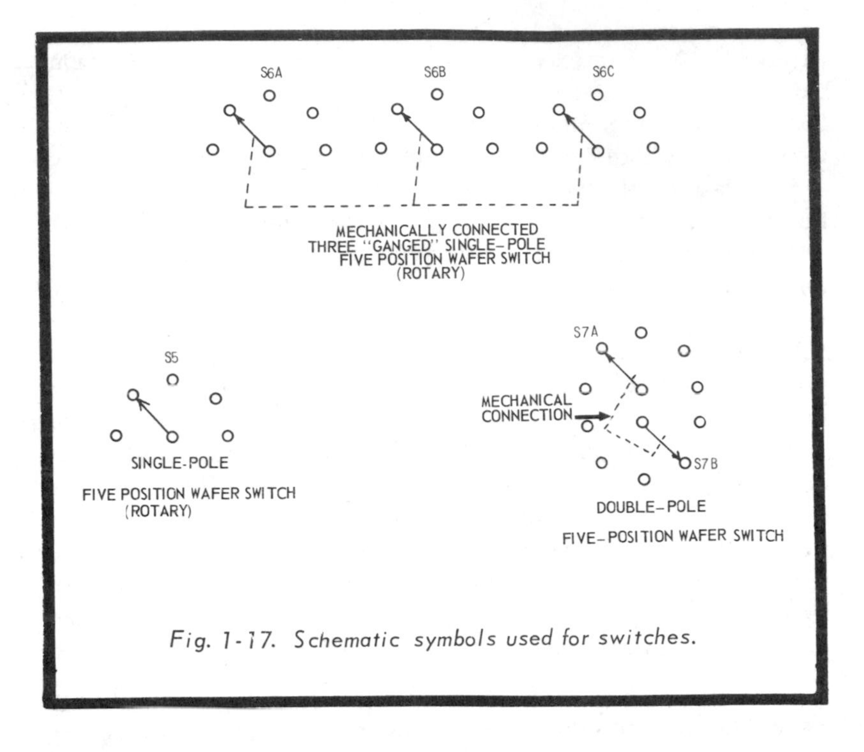


*Fig. 1-17. Schematic symbols used for switches.*

tively minor expense. Dry cells, because of their chemical makeup, cannot be recharged.

A type of rechargeable battery which can be used in flashlights, portable radios, and electronic equipment is the nickel-cadmium battery. Other dry-cell batteries now available for low-power operation such as in flashlights and transistor radios are the mercury and alkaline cells. The mercury battery is more expensive than the ordinary dry-cell flashlight battery, but it can be stored for a much longer time and its output voltage is more constant. The alkaline battery is also more expensive than the ordinary carbon-zinc dry cell, but it is capable of a much longer life.

## SWITCHES

Everytime you turn on a radio or start your car, you are making an electrical connection through a switch. The courtesy light in your automobile comes on because a door switch closes and so does the light in your refrigerator. Pushbutton switches are used in such applications. Since the switch completes only a single circuit between the light and a power source, it is known as a single-pole switch. The schematic symbol is shown in Fig. 1-17. Switches are available in toggle, knife, pushbutton, slide, and rotary selector or wafer types.

Many switches have multiple contacts to complete many circuits at once or to connect one point in the circuit to any one of several circuits. Regardless of the type of switch, they are all identified on a schematic with the letter "S," for example: S1, S2, or S3. "Ganged" switch sections are labeled S1A, S1B, etc. The schematic symbol for multiple-contact switches is also shown in Fig. 1-17.

As illustrated, a single-pole single-throw switch is the most basic and the type you are likely to find as a part of a radio or TV volume control. A single-pole double-throw (SPDT) switch is used to provide a connection from one main contact to either of two circuit contacts. A double-pole double-throw (DPDT) switch is actually two single-pole double-throw

*Fig. 1-18. Pictured here are two popular switches—a slide-operated and a rocker-type switch.*

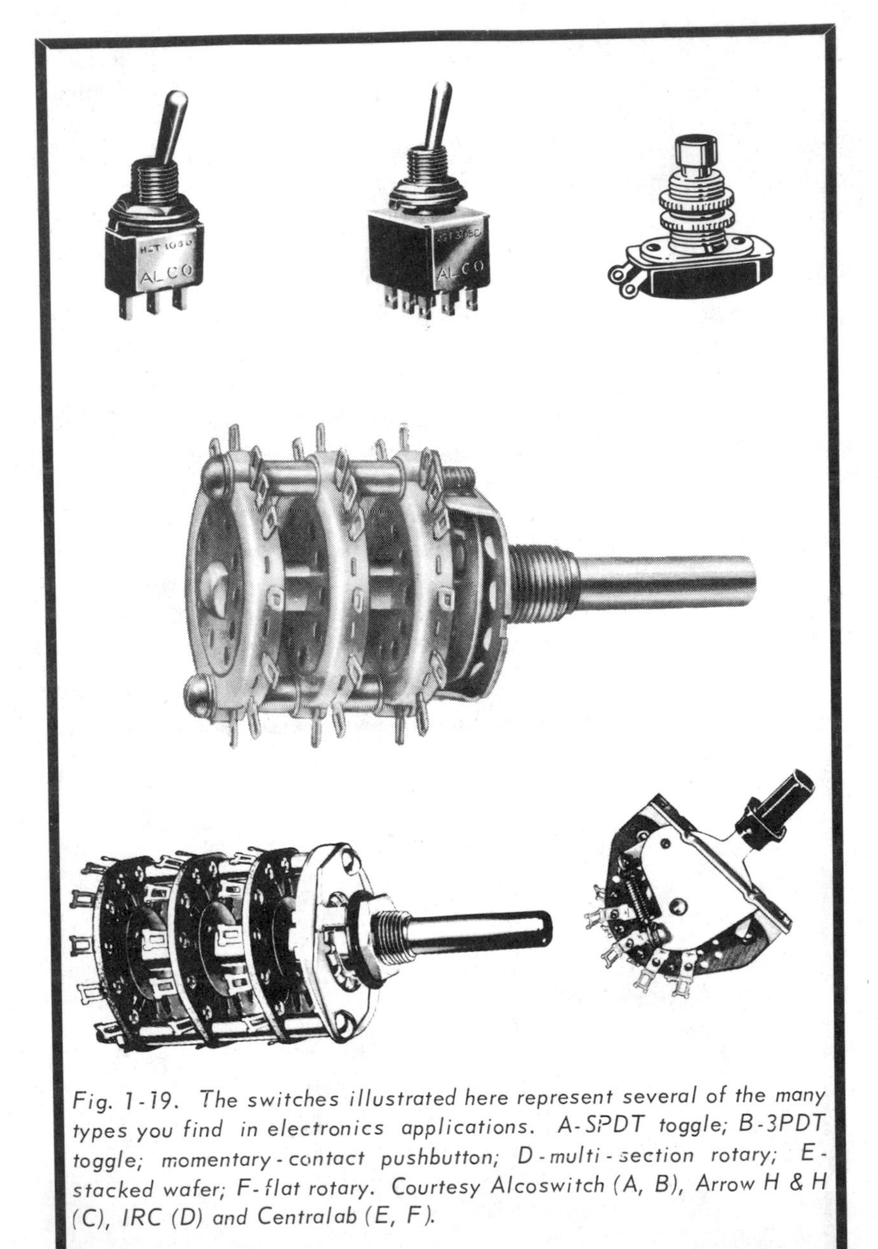


*Fig. 1-19. The switches illustrated here represent several of the many types you find in electronics applications. A-SPDT toggle; B-3PDT toggle; momentary-contact pushbutton; D-multi-section rotary; E-stacked wafer; F-flat rotary. Courtesy Alcoswitch (A, B), Arrow H & H (C), IRC (D) and Centralab (E, F).*

switches mechanically connected or "ganged." DPDT switches (as well as others) are available as slide-operated, toggle, knife, etc., depending on the application. Fig. 1-18 pictures slide and rocker type switches. In electronic circuits which require multiple connections, a rotary selector or wafer switch is normally used (Fig. 1-19). The combinations and applications for this type of switch are unlimited. Wafer switches may also be "ganged" or mechanically connected.

## RELAYS

In the discussion of switches, we said that a switch is used to complete a circuit or circuits. A relay is a switch too, but it is operated electronically or electrically—not manually. We can best illustrate the way a relay works by referring to the diagram and schematic symbols shown in Figs. 1-20 and 1-21. As shown, the relay has an iron core coil and an "armature" which is mechanically connected to a set of contacts. The spring attached to the armature pulls the contacts open when the relay current is interrupted. The schematic symbol is basically the same for all relays. The only variation is in the number and arrangement of the contacts.

The reference letter designation for a relay is "K"; the contacts themselves are usually numbered, too. The single-pole relay (SP) has only one set of contacts. Relay contacts may be either made to open or close, depending on how they are arranged. Contacts that open when the relay is not operating or energized are called "normally-open" and labeled

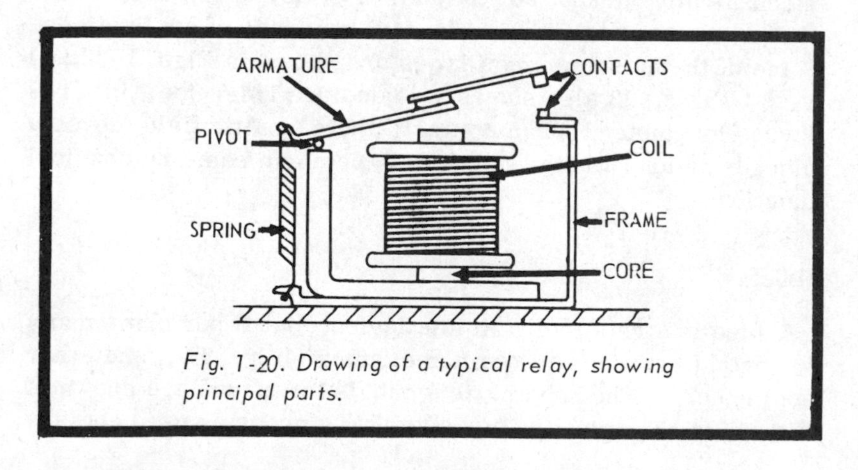


*Fig. 1-20. Drawing of a typical relay, showing principal parts.*

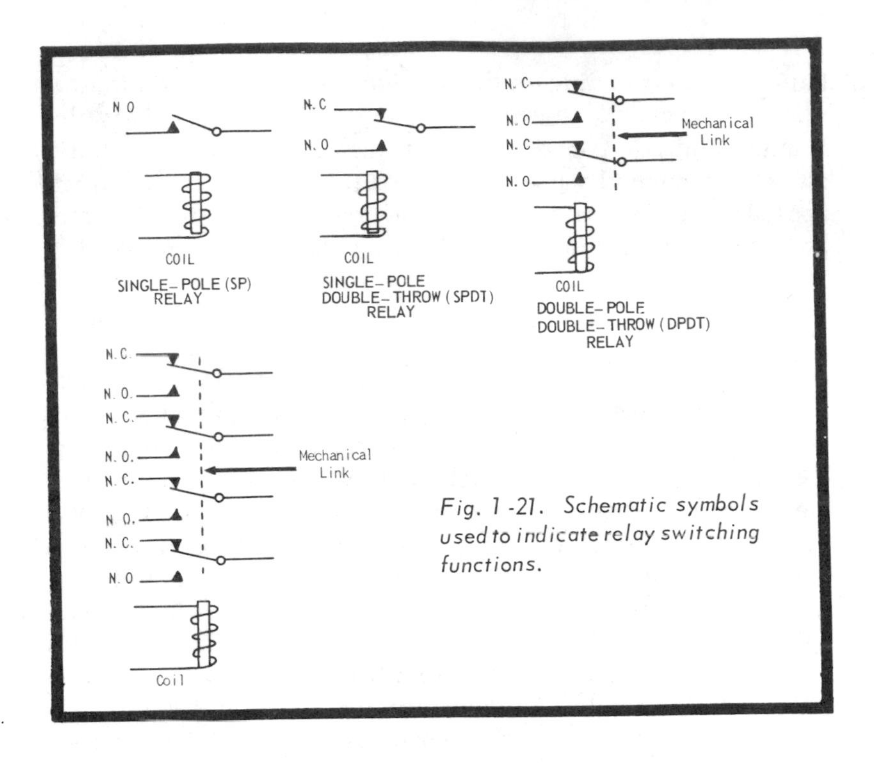


*Fig. 1-21. Schematic symbols used to indicate relay switching functions.*

N.O. on the schematic symbol. Contacts that are closed when the relay is not energized are called "normally-closed" and labeled N.C. on the schematic.

As illustrated, a relay can have many contacts to perform several switching functions at one time. The contacts are mechanically linked so they all close (or open) at the same time. Relays are available for hundreds of applications. Some of the more common types are shown in Figs. 1-22 and 1-23. Fig. 1-23 also shows a solenoid. This, too, is a relay. But instead of a contact, the magnetic field moves a plunger or arm which is used to perform some mechanical function.

## FUSES

A fuse is a relatively simple device, but it performs many important functions in your home, automobile, TV, and other appliances. The schematic symbols for a fuse are shown in Fig. 1-24. The types of fuses you have probably used and are

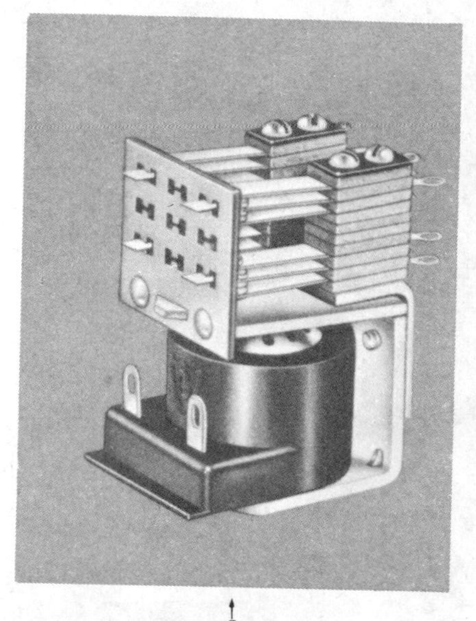

*Fig. 1-22. Relays are available for a wide range of switching applications. The general purpose relay (A) is a 4-pole double-throw, as os the sealed plug-in type (B). The miniature relay (C) is designed for application where space is at a premium. Courtesy Guardian Electric (A,B) and General Electric.*

most familiar with are shown in Figs. 1-25 and 1-26. Glass cartridge fuses are normally used in TV, hi-fi, and automobile fuse panels, while the screw-in type is generally found in home fuse boxes and in heavy appliances.

All fuses "operate" (or open) on the same principle—heat. You know when you turn the lights on in your home that they are drawing a certain amount of current. The AC outlets and

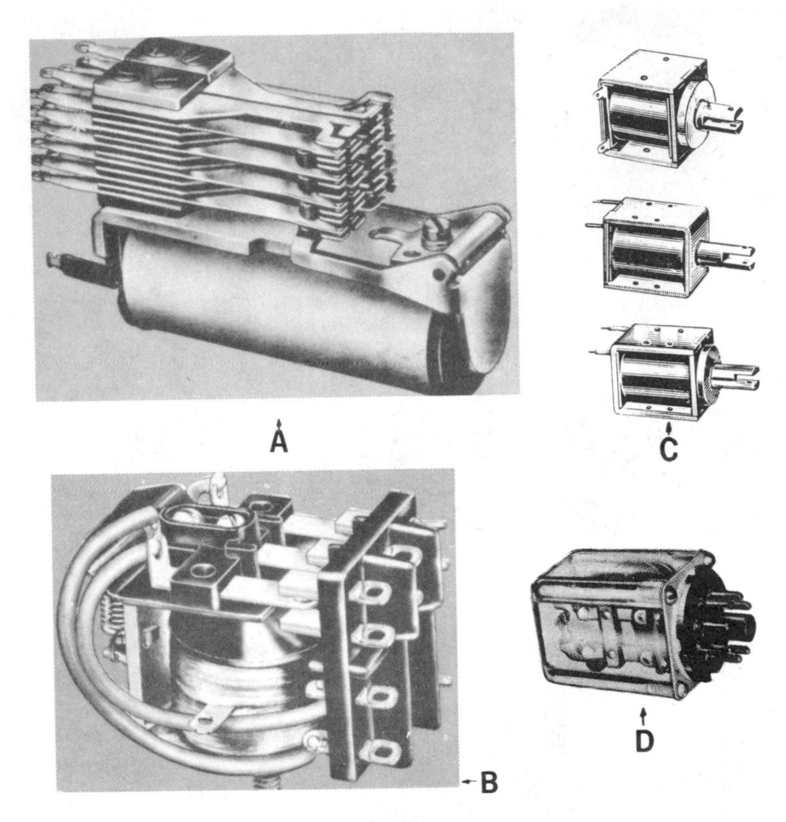


*Fig. 1-23. Here are several more types of relay-telephones (A), a general-purpose (B) a plug-in mounted on an octal-type tube base (C) and several solenoids (D). Courtesy Potter & Brumfield (A, B, C) and Guardian (D).*

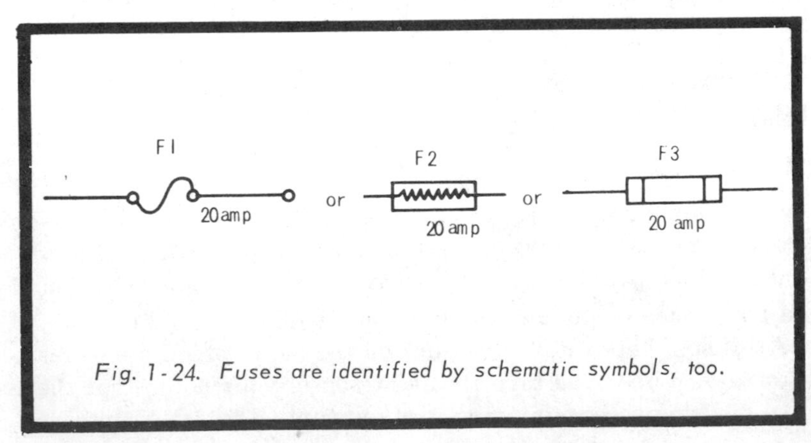


*Fig. 1-24. Fuses are identified by schematic symbols, too.*

ceiling fixtures are wired in a number of branch circuits, each protected by a fuse of the required rating. If you were to look at the fuse panel, you would see that each fuse perhaps takes care of two or three rooms or circuits. If you overloaded a circuit by plugging in more appliances than it can handle, the current going through the fuse will melt the fuse element and open the circuit. The fuse element is nothing more than metal alloy which has a low melting temperature. The higher the fuse rating, the larger the element.

The fuses in your television set and automobile work the

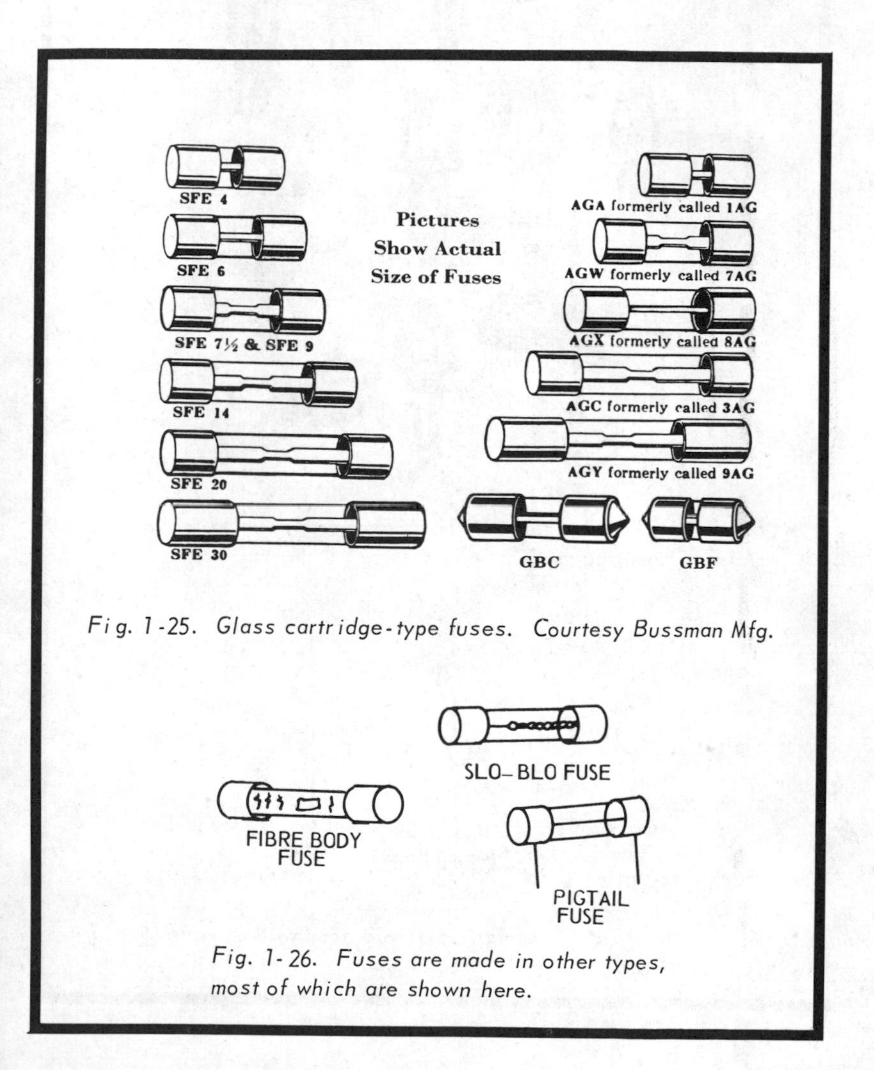


*Fig. 1-25. Glass cartridge-type fuses. Courtesy Bussman Mfg.*

*Fig. 1-26. Fuses are made in other types, most of which are shown here.*

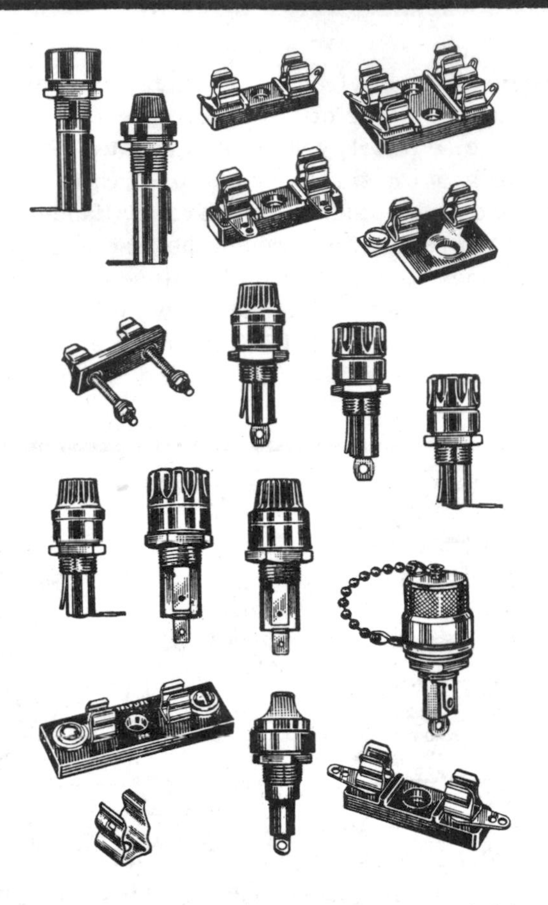

*Fig. 1-27. The fuseholders shown here are intended for various chassis-mounting applications.*

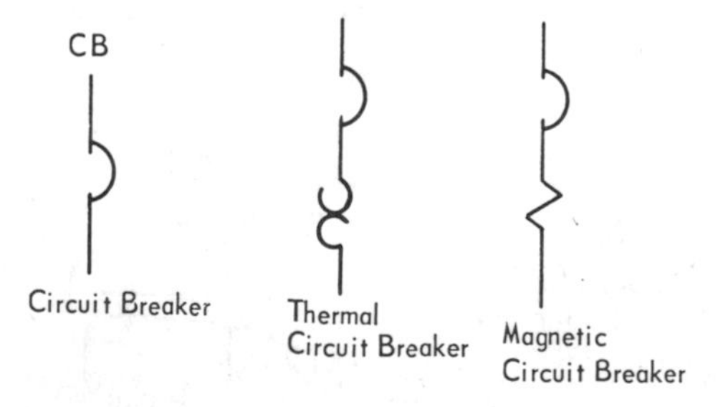


*Fig. 1-28. Schematic symbols used to designate circuit breakers.*

same way, except they are physically different. Since fuses are designed to protect an appliance or wiring, it is dangerous to replace a fuse with one rated higher than the original.

The fuses used in your home fuse panel are screw-in types such as shown in Fig. 1-26. Cartridge-type fuses shown in Fig. 1-25 are plug-in or clip-in types which are made to fit in specially designed holders or clips (Fig. 1-27). Some fuses are wired into the circuit and have leads connected to them for this purpose. The pigtail fuse in Fig. 1-26 is an example. The trend toward miniaturization and the increased use of transistors has also created a need for miniature versions of pigtail fuses.

Another commonly used fuse is the "slo-blow" fuse. It has a special element with a built-in time delay for use in circuits where there may be a momentary high surge of current when the equipment is first turned on. Motor-starting circuits and some electronic equipment power supplies have an initial surge or overloaded current which is higher than the normal operating current. Since the surge is sometimes two or three times the normal current, it would be dangerous to fuse it at that rating. So, we use a slo-blow fuse which will hold until the surge passes and then safely protect the circuit at its normal current rating.

## CIRCUIT BREAKERS

The schematic symbols for circuit breakers are shown in Fig. 1-28, with some of the more common types illustrated

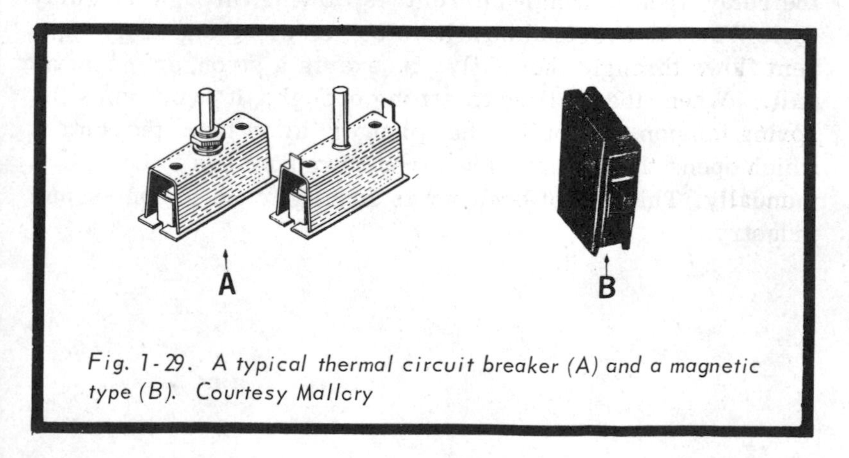


*Fig. 1-29. A typical thermal circuit breaker (A) and a magnetic type (B). Courtesy Mallory*

in Fig. 1-29. Circuit breakers have become popular replacements for fuses in many applications such as in home wiring, television sets, and industrial circuits. Circuit breakers may be either thermally- or magnetically-operated.

A circuit breaker differs from a fuse in that it does not burn out or need to be replaced after an overload condition. It is an electromechanical device. Thermal circuit breakers are made with a special type of metal strip (called "bi-metal") that touches a contact arm and completes the circuit. This bi-metal strip has a specific rating and as long as the current is within limits it will remain in position against the contact arm. If the current goes over the normal rating, heat will cause the bi-metal strip to bend away from the contact arm and open the circuit. Depending on what kind of thermal circuit breaker it is, it may be re-set mechanically or it may re-set itself automatically. The mechanical re-set units are pushbutton operated (see Fig. 1-29). Breakers that re-set themselves automatically have no button. As the bi-metal strip cools, it automatically returns to the closed-circuit position.

The magnetic circuit breaker does the same kind of job a thermal unit does, only it operates something like a relay. Its symbol is shown in Fig. 1-28. Remember our explanation of a relay coil; when current flows through the coil, it creates a magnetic field which closes the contacts. The magnetic breaker operates about the same, except instead of contacts it uses a plunger, like a solenoid. The plunger makes contact to complete the circuit, held in place by a spring which has just the right amount of tension to overcome the pull of the relay when normal current is flowing through the relay coil. When an overload condition comes along and more current flows through the coil, it exerts a stronger magnetic pull. When the pull gets strong enough, it overcomes the spring tension and pulls the plunger away from the contact which opens the circuit. The circuit breaker has to be re-set manually. This type of breaker is usually found in homes and industry.

## CHAPTER 2

# Transducers, Indicating & Miscellaneous Components

In addition to the "discrete," individual circuit components covered in Chapter 1, there are those which change sound or mechanical movement into electrical facsimiles and vice versa, and those which provide aural or visual "indications," such as meters. Although some of these components are normally found only in special equipments, a complete knowledge of what each item looks like both physically and on a schematic, will help you better understand a schematic diagram.

### CRYSTALS

The exact definition of a crystal can be pretty difficult to understand without some background in physics. But briefly and simply, a crystal is made from a solid, such as quartz, barium titanate, or Rochelle salt. These particular solids are used because they have "piezoelectric" properties. A crystal is cut from quartz somewhat like cutting a precious gem. When a crystal is cut in a certain way, it will vibrate at a specific frequency when voltage is applied in an electronic circuit. And so, crystals can be and are used to control the frequency of many types of oscillators, such as those found in CB transmitters, signal generators, color TV sets, FM receivers, plus hundreds of other circuits. The reason crystals are so popular for frequency control is because their vibrating frequency is very stable, especially under controlled voltage and temperature conditions.

Crystals are shown on schematic diagrams by the symbol illustrated in Fig. 2-1. The schematic letter designation is the letter "X," although the letter "Y" is sometimes used. Fig. 2-2 shows the physical appearance of several types of crystals. The most commonly used crystals in consumer electronics equipment are of the plug-in or wired-in miniature type. Some

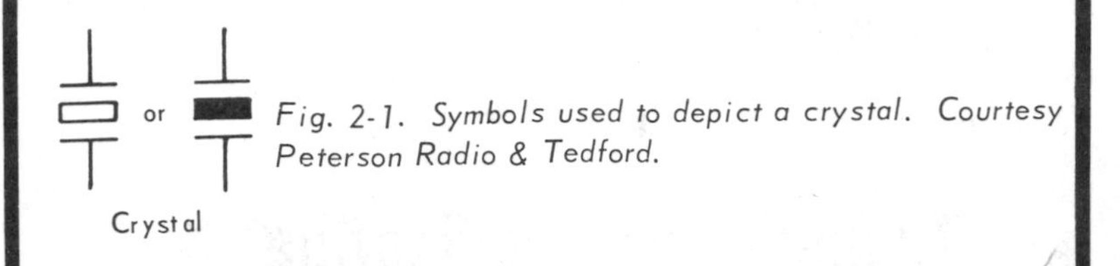


*Fig. 2-1. Symbols used to depict a crystal. Courtesy Peterson Radio & Tedford.*

*Fig. 2-2. Crystal units such as these are quite common in certain types of electronic gear.*

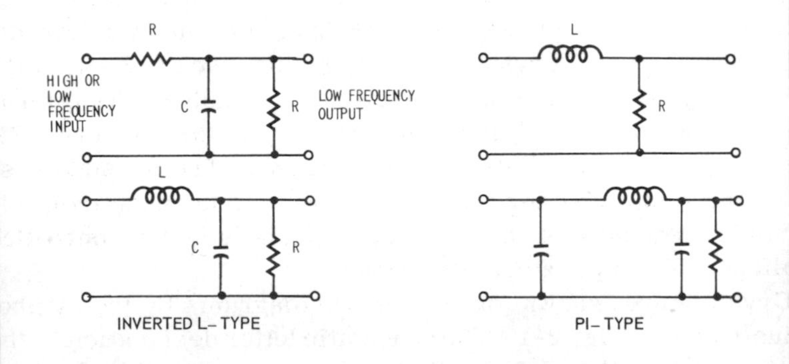


*Fig. 2-3. Typical low-pass filter networks.*

communications equipment uses a larger type of plug-in crystal while other equipments use heated crystal units. The heated or oven-controlled crystal unit is generally built in a sealed container which plugs into a socket supplying heater voltage and crystal connections. In tube-type equipment the crystal heater or oven is similar to a tube filament and, in fact, it may receive its voltage from the filament line.

Crystal ovens often have a built-in thermostat consisting of two bi-metal strips as in the circuit breaker discussed in Chapter 1. These strips are contacts which, when closed, operate a heater-voltage control circuit. When the operating temperature is exceeded, the strips or contacts separate and open the heater supply. Then the bi-metal contacts cool until they again close and complete the heater circuit.

## FILTERS

The word "filter" should be familiar. Your automobile engine has an oil filter, the wife's washer has a lint filter, and some cigarettes have a tar and nicotine filter. They all do the same thing—they allow only certain signals to pass. Filters come in many styles and designs for as many applications. We won't get involved in their respective characteristics, but the schematic symbols for most of the various types should be helpful.

Generally, filters are made from a network of resistors, inductors, capacitors, or a combination of these, depending on the application. Crystals are also used for filter networks, as are mechanical devices. Filter networks using resistors, inductors, or capacitors are termed as "low-pass" or "high-pass" filters. These are shown in Figs. 2-3 and 2-4.

The entire network making up the filter circuit is sometimes enclosed in a shielded case as shown on the schematic diagram in Fig. 2-5 by dashed lines around the circuit. A mechanical filter is almost always designed as a sealed unit and shown on the schematic simply as a box with input and output terminals (see Fig. 2-6). It is designated as "FL" and its frequency is given as shown. Crystal filters are also generally sealed units, as their tolerance and design make them extremely critical. Attempting to repair them in the field is normally not recommended. The schematic symbol for a crystal filter may be a box identified in the same manner as a mechanical filter, or

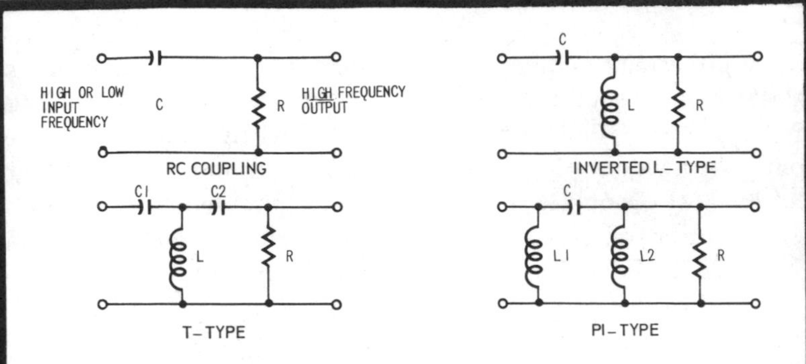


*Fig. 2-4. Basic high-pass filter networks.*

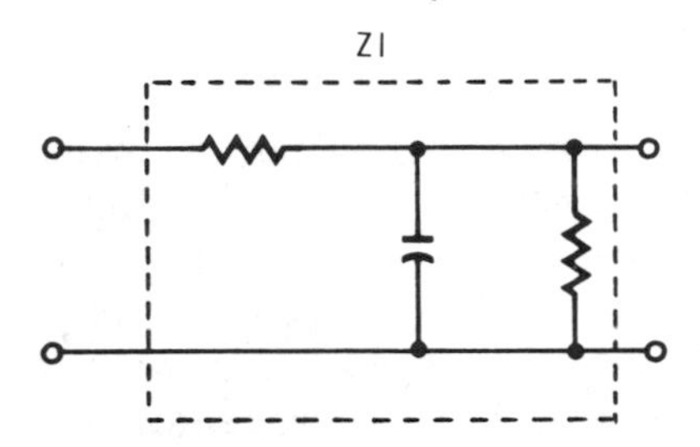


*Fig. 2-5. Filter networks are often shielded by a metal enclosure as indicated by the broken line on this schematic.*

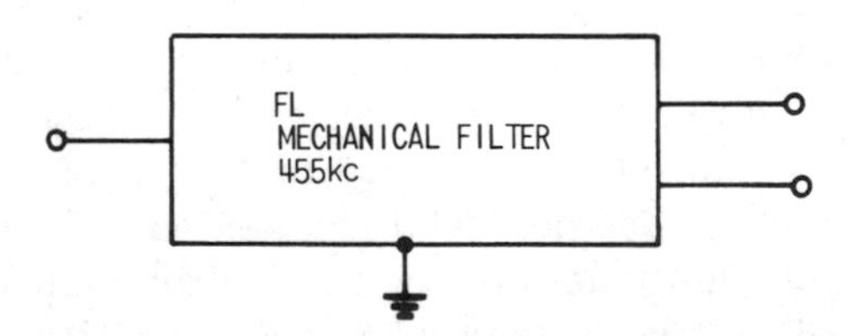


*Fig. 2-6. Sometimes, mechanical filters are represented as a box with terminals, as shown here.*

it may show actual circuit connections (see Fig. 2-7). Crystal and mechanical filters are found in communications transceivers where an extremely high degree of selectivity is required, especially in single-shielded transmitting and receiving units.

## HEADPHONES

Headphones, sometimes called earphones and headsets, are normally not shown on a schematic diagram of a particular piece of electronic equipment. But headphone accessory jacks are built into many of the products we use every day, such as our TV, portable radio, stereo, and many communications receivers. The schematic symbols for the various types of headphones are shown in Fig. 2-8.

A headphone may be classified as crystal, dynamic, or magnetic, depending upon the construction of the transducer or sound-reproducing element. The schematic symbol does not indicate this, but a footnote may be included if a specific type of headphone is required. Generally, a dynamic headphone will be used where high fidelity and low-impedance (4 to 8 ohms) is necessary. Magnetic headphones are high impedance, usually 2000 ohms or more, and can be placed directly in the plate circuit of an amplifier tube or the collector circuit of a transistor. Most headphones are available in either single or double units.

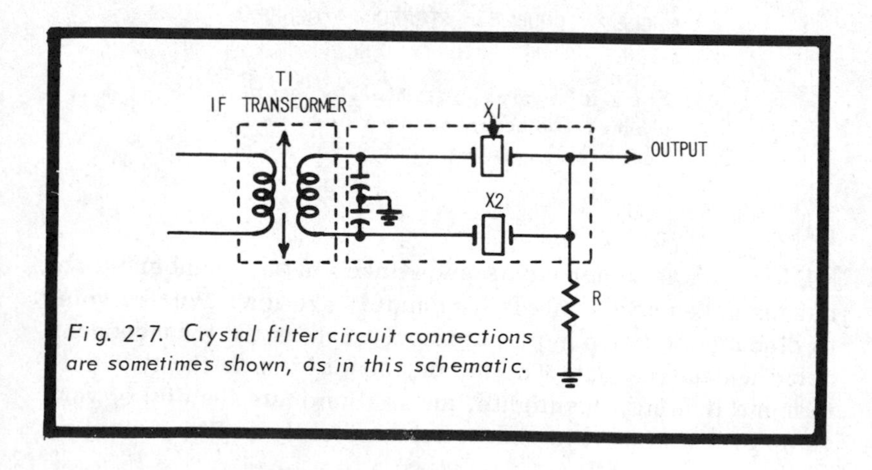


*Fig. 2-7. Crystal filter circuit connections are sometimes shown, as in this schematic.*

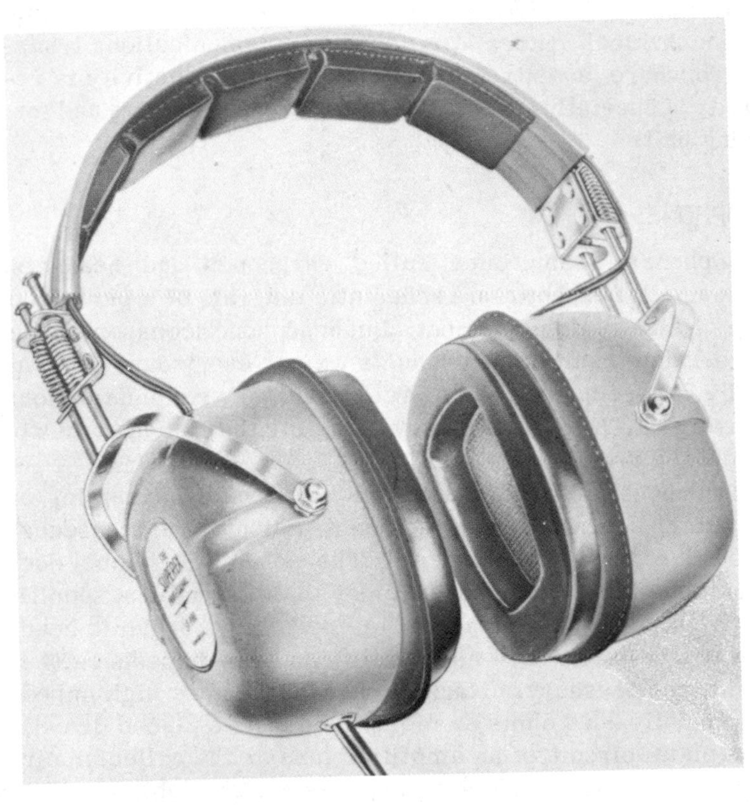

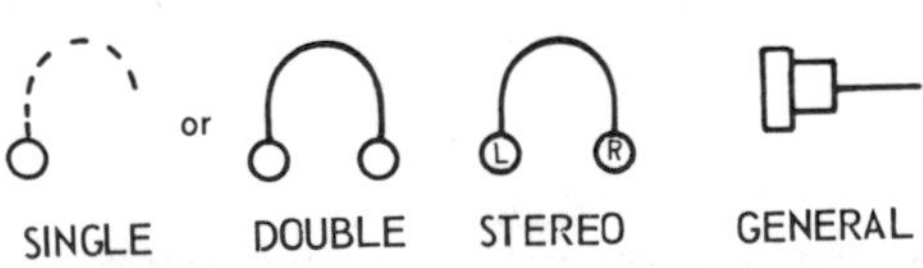


*Fig. 2-8. Schematic symbol for headphones. The headphone is a stereo unit. Courtesy Superex.*

## LAMPS

Lamps are as numerous as snowflakes in a November storm, but the schematic symbols fortunately are few. We are going to discuss the types most common, such as the incandescent, neon, and the readout. The incandescent lamp is the type used in home lighting, flashlights, and to illuminate the dial of your radio or TV set. It is shown schematically in Fig. 2-9.

Incandescent lamps come with many types of bases and in many voltage ratings. The base may be a screw-type, bayonet, candelabra, or wire leads. The letter designation for a lamp is the letter "L."

Neon lamps have more specific uses because they are gas-filled and come on only when a certain voltage is applied. When a neon lamp turns on, it is said to be "ionized." The voltage necessary to ionize a neon lamp is generally around 65 volts or more and they are most often used as indicators in specilized equipment. However, you will also find these devices used in relaxation oscillators and waveform generating circuits. The schematic symbol for a neon lamp is shown in Fig. 2-10.

A readout lamp or indicator is another special type of device. It is used as a numerical display indicator in digital counters, voltmeters, and other similar units. The schematic diagram for a readout indicator is shown in Fig. 2-11. It is much like a tube in appearance, but it has many cathodes. The cathodes are made in the physical shape of a number which lights or glows when voltage is applied to it. Many of these readout

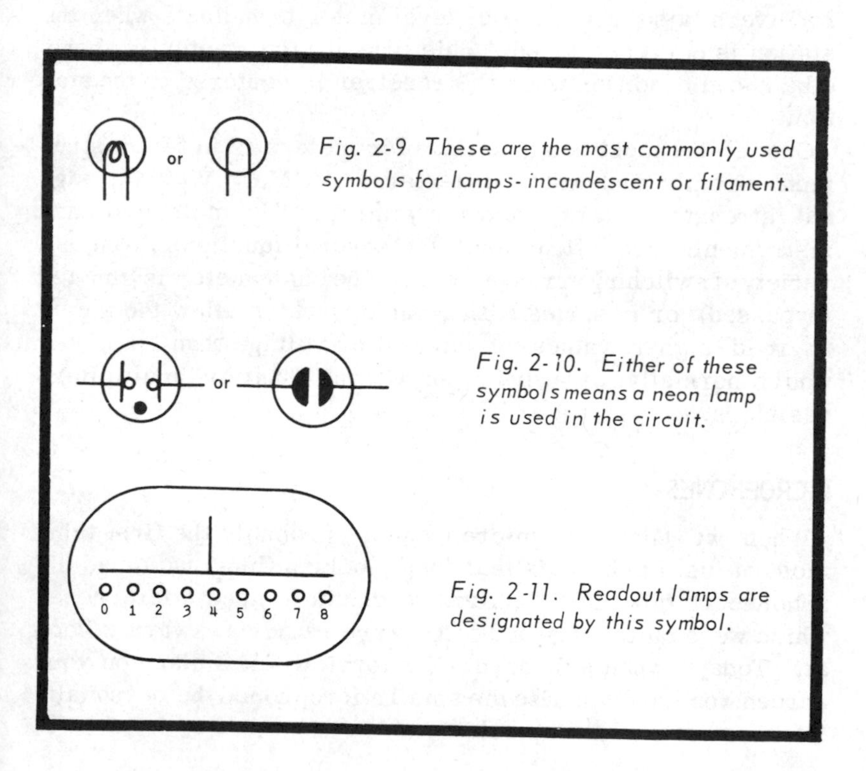


Fig. 2-9 These are the most commonly used symbols for lamps- incandescent or filament.

Fig. 2-10. Either of these symbols means a neon lamp is used in the circuit.

Fig. 2-11. Readout lamps are designated by this symbol.

units are gas-filled neon, while others use incandescent lamps in a special arrangement to provide numerals or letters.

## METERS

Most schematics simply show a meter as a circle surrounding a letter which designates whether the meter is for measuring voltage (v), current (a), signal levels, (db) or other. As shown in Fig. 2-12, the polarity at which the meter is connected in the circuit is given on the respective terminals.

In most circuits, meters are installed to monitor specific values of voltage, current, or signal. In some circuits, such as in transmitters, an ammeter may be used to monitor several circuits by connecting the meter to these circuits through a switching arrangement. In tape recorders, however, a signal-level meter is normally connected to monitor the incoming level on only one channel. Stereo recorders have one level meter for each of the two channels. Some stereo FM receivers also use a signal level meter to indicate when the station is correctly tuned. This type of meter actually shows a balanced condition when the receiver is centered on the station.

One of the most common uses for meters is in test instrument circuits such as tube testers, VOMs, VTVMs, signal strength meters, and many more. The meters in such instruments are often used for several functions through a variety of switching arrangements. The basic meter is shunted (bypassed) or in series with resistors which allow the meter to read higher values of current or voltage than the meter would normally be capable of without shunt or "multiplier" resistors.

## MICROPHONES

When we speak of microphones, probably the first thing most of us think of is that funny looking thing radio and TV announcers talk into. Earlier broadcasters used microphones which were quite large and some were rather awkward to look at. Today, when a modern TV interview takes place on your screen you hardly notice the small microphones the personalities wear around their necks.

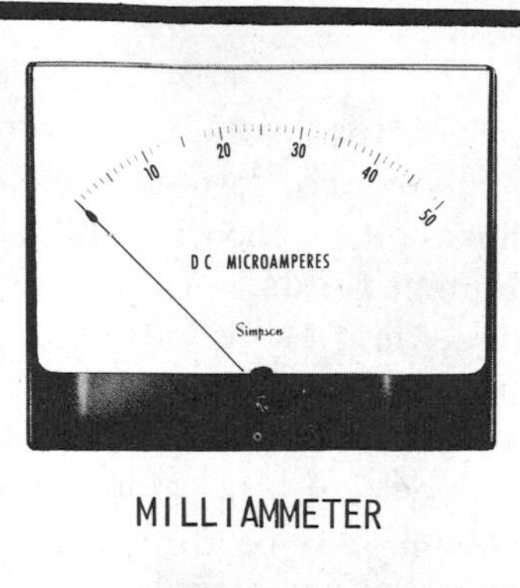


MILLIAMMETER

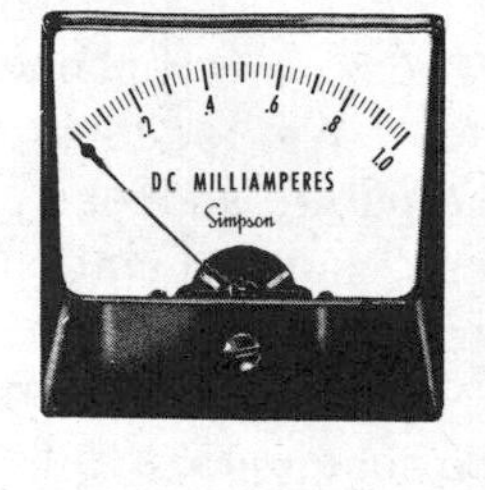

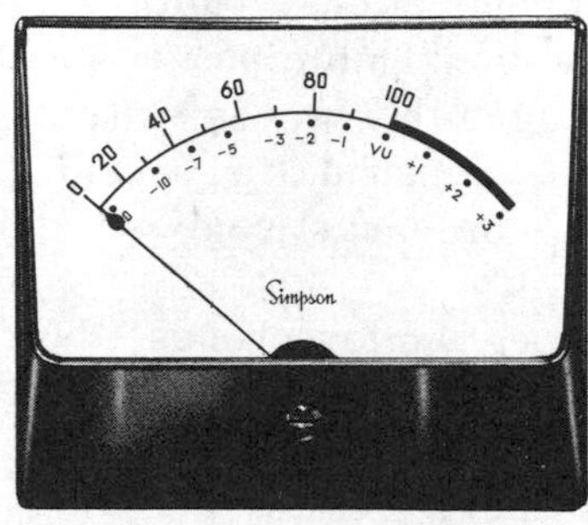


VU SIGNAL LEVEL

GALVANOMETER

AC VOLTMETER

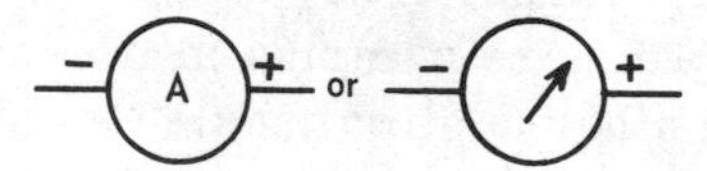


A=Ammeter
MA=Milliammeter
V=Voltmeter
db=Decibel Meter

*Fig. 2 – 12. Circles with letters indicate the use of a meter and its function. Several basic movements are shown, Courtesy Simpson.*

Today, microphones in one way or another, affect everyone's life. We use them for our tape recorders, two-way radios, and public address systems in churches, schools, and business, not to mention the entertainment fields. A microphone turns sound, either music or voice, into electrical energy.

Naturally, there are many types of microphones, but again, the schematic symbols are few. As shown in Fig. 2-13, microphone symbols indicate whether the device is a "general" type or directional. "General" microphones may be almost any type such as those used for radio communications, public address, and home entertainment. A directional microphone picks up only sounds directly in front of it. In other words, a directional microphone will not pick up noise or sound from behind. They are used by most entertainers, broadcast studios, and recording companies.

Even though there are many types of microphones, their job is basically the same—to change sound into electrical energy. A microphone has in its mouthpiece an element which performs this change; it is called a "transducer." One of the things that makes a particular microphone better than another for a certain job is the material used in the transducer. Some of the more common types of microphones are the crystal, ceramic, dynamic, carbon, and condenser.

A crystal microphone uses a piezoelectric element like the crystals previously mentioned, and it usually provides a fairly high output voltage. Ceramic microphones are more rugged than crystal types but operate in the same way. Dynamic types are popular in many applications, but their output voltage is relatively low. Carbon microphones are also rugged and have a very high output voltage. They also have a limited frequency response and are more common in two-way radio communications than in other applications. Condenser types, on the other hand, are used in applications where wide frequency response is needed, such as for music and recording.

## PHONO PICKUPS

Phono pickups or phono cartridges change the mechanical vibrations in the groove of a record into electrical signals. When a record is made, the record-cutting head changes the sound picked up by studio microphones, amplifiers, etc., into mechanical vibrations. A needle in the cutting head cuts these vibrations into record groves corresponding to the sounds.

A phono pickup or cartridge needle simply follows the mechanical vibrations in the record groove to change them back into electrical signals which are reproduced and amplified to sound as much like the original as possible. A monaural or single-channel recording has vibrations in one "plank" and a single element pickup is used. In stereo reproduction the side walls and depth of the record groove are used to record vibrations. The dual-element stereo pickup then receives vibrations from the walls as well as from the depth of the groove.

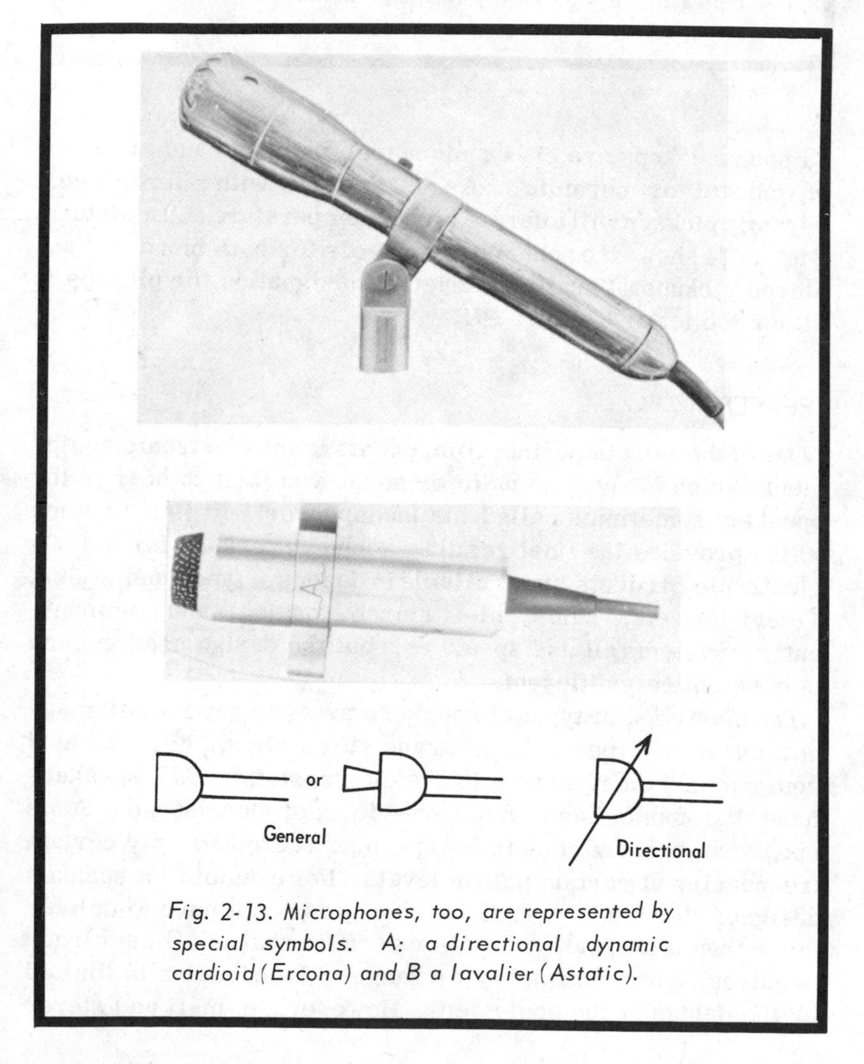


*Fig. 2-13. Microphones, too, are represented by special symbols. A: a directional dynamic cardioid (Ercona) and B a lavalier (Astatic).*

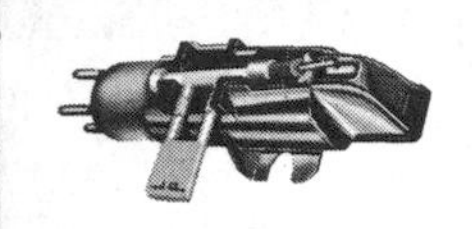

*Fig. 2-14. Phono pickup symbols usually indicate whether they are monaural or stereo. The three cartridges shown represent the wide variety available now.*

Phono pickups are either monaural or stereo and are made of crystal or ceramic. As is the case with microphones, ceramic pickups will tolerate higher temperature and moisture. Fig. 2-14 shows the schematic symbols for both monaural and stereo pickups. Usually, the letter designation for pickups is either the letter "P" or "PU."

## SPEAKERS

One of the most important components in any electronic equipment which provides audio or sound you want to hear is the speaker (sometimes called the loudspeaker). It is the device which provides the final result—sound. Speakers for today's electronic products are available in dozens of types and styles. Television sets, radios, hi-fi stereo, paging, and communications systems all use speakers, but the design used in each may be entirely different.

The most popular types of speakers are the permanent magnet dynamic type used in transistor radios, TV, and hi fi equipment. Another type is the electrostatic. All speakers have the same basic function—to reproduce sound. Some speakers, because of their design, can reproduce only certain frequencies at certain power levels. For example, a speaker designed for a TV or radio normally does not have to deliver more than a few watts of power because that is all the circuit requires. Also, the fidelity or range of frequencies is limited by the design of the equipment. However, in hi-fi and stereo equipment, the power levels may run to almost 100 watts and the speakers must be able to reproduce sound from very low bass notes to an extremely high audio frequency range.

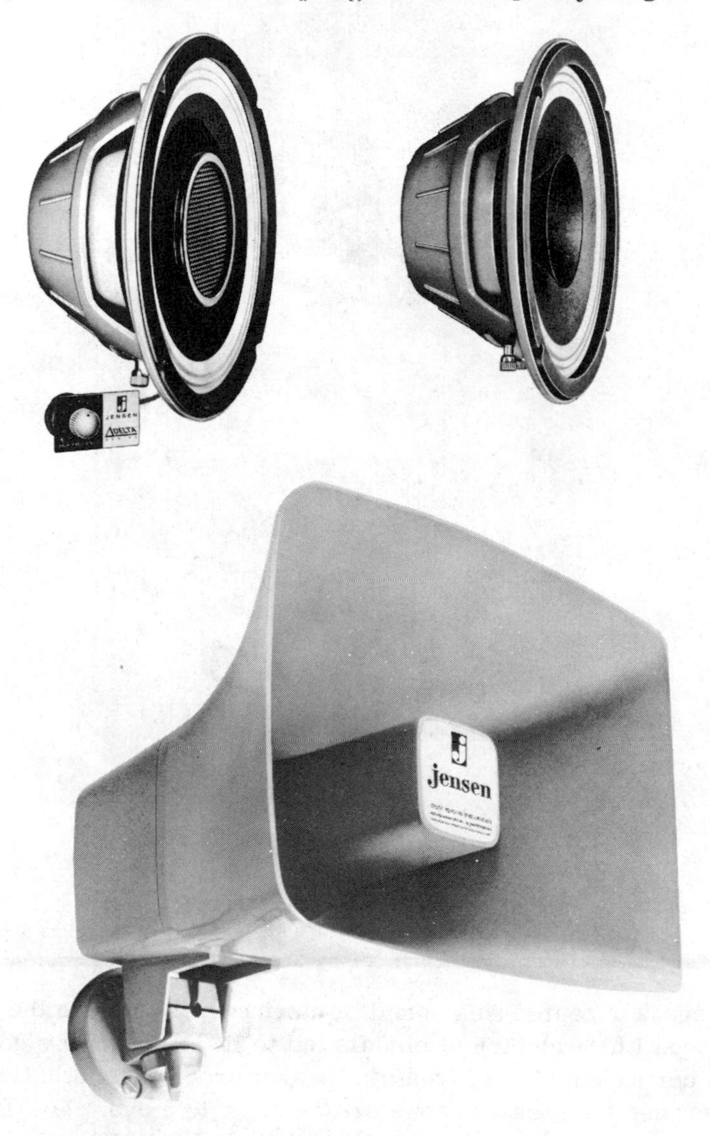


*Fig. 2-15. Speaker or loudspeaker symbols simply indicate the use of a speaker, not the type. The horn-shaped unit is a compression type. Courtesy Jensen.*

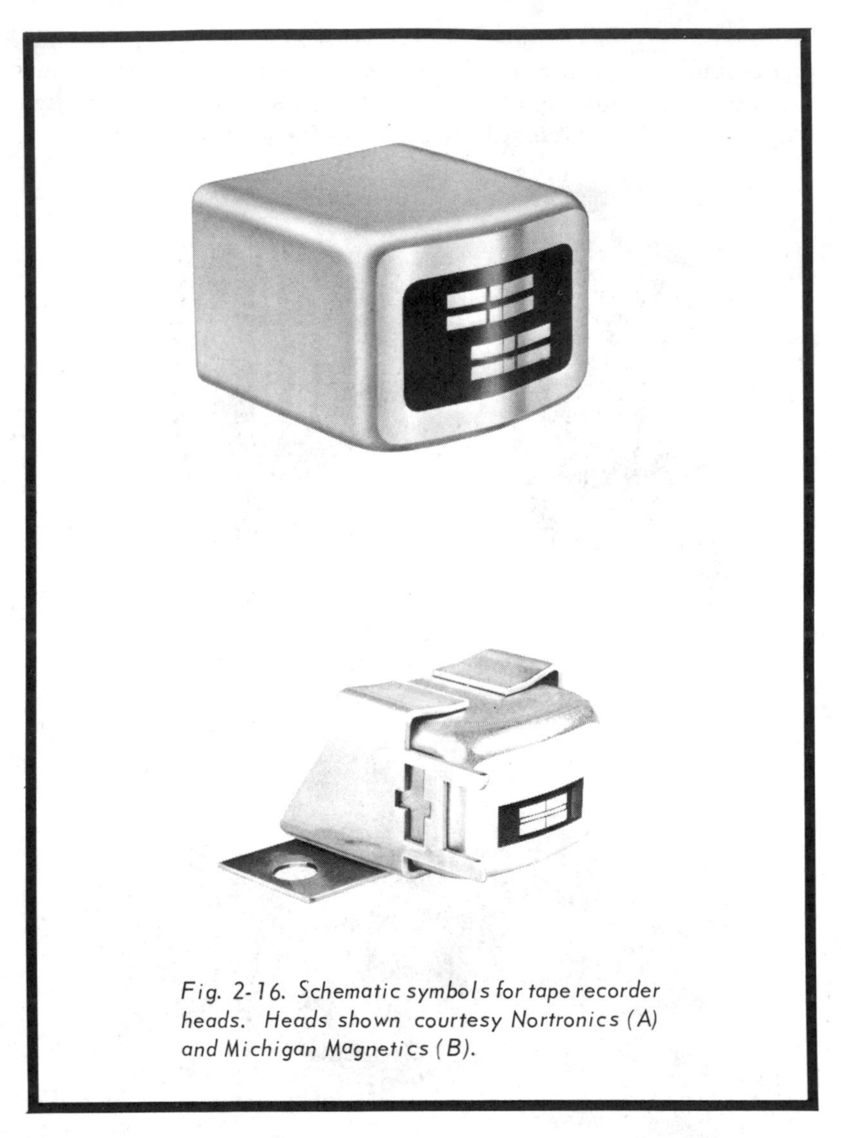

*Fig. 2-16. Schematic symbols for tape recorder heads. Heads shown courtesy Nortronics (A) and Michigan Magnetics (B).*

A speaker reproduces sound by mechanically moving the air in step with the electrical signals fed to it. Electrical signals to a permanent magnet dynamic speaker create magnetic fields that cause the speaker cone or diaphram to move. Low frequencies require a large movement of air and the higher in frequency the sounds become, the smaller the air movement is.

Since fidelity and power are not critical in general speaker applications such as TV and radio, a standard type of dynamic speaker is often suitable. However, in high-powered, wide-frequency range stereo equipment, special speakers are used, one for low frequency, one for middle-range frequencies, and one for the highs. Such speakers are called the "woofer," "mid-range," and "tweeter," respectively. Some systems combine speakers in a single case to provide the necessary coverage. A two-speaker combination is called a "coaxial" which generally has a woofer and a tweeter. A three-speaker combination is called a "triaxial" and includes the woofer, mid-range, and tweeter.

The schematic symbols for speakers, shown in Fig. 2-15, indicate only individual speakers, so a symbol for coaxial and triaxial units would have to have two and three speaker symbols. The symbol does not indicate the type of speaker. Letter designations for speakers are usually SPKR, SP, S and LS (LS means loudspeaker).

## TAPE RECORDER HEADS

A tape recorder head is used to convert electrical signals into a magnetic field which varies with the input signal. The magnetic field in turn magnetizes the tape as it passes across the head. Schematic symbols for tape heads are shown in Fig. 2-16.

Just as a recording tape head magnetizes the tape in accord with the input signal, a playback head picks up the pre-recorded variations and sends them to an amplifier for reproduction into sound. The schematic symbols for these heads are the same, but the letter designation indicates the function. For example, a playback head will be designated "P" while a record head will be indicated "R." In some cases, the same head is designed to provide both functions and it will be designated "R/P." A tape recorder also uses a third head called the "erase" head. Its purpose is to erase any previously recorded material on the tape before it reaches the recording head.

The erase head, located in front of the recording head, provides a high-frequency magnetic field which alternately increases and decreases to eliminate previous tape magnetization. The erase head is indicated by the same symbol used for record and playback, but the letter designation is the letter "E."

CHAPTER 3

# Solid-State Devices

Solid-state devices, or semiconductors as they are commonly called, are used today instead of tubes in many electronic products. There are several reasons why solid-state devices have gained such popularity in the electronics industry. Among the most important are that they require less power to operate, they are smaller in size, cost less, and last longer.

It is an interesting fact that solid-state devices have only recently gained tremendous popularity. And yet, the earliest radio receivers used cat-whisker crystal detectors which were solid-state devices. For many years, obviously, the semiconductor field was dormant. But with the advances now being made in the state of the art, solid-state devices will likely replace all of the functions now fulfilled by vacuum tubes.

Semiconductors are made of either germanium or silicon which contains impurities to produce an N- and P-type material. A transistor has both N- and P-type regions and these are the materials which allow current and hole flow. The actual physics behind the operation of solid-state devices is much more complicated. But for the purpose of understanding semiconductor placement in a circuit, the P-type material is considered positive and the N-type, negative.

## TRANSISTORS

One of the most common solid-state devices is the transistor. Because of its advantages it is now used in every type of electronic circuit, with more uses being found each day. Basically, transistors come in two types—NPN and PNP. These are shown schematically in Fig. 3-1. The letter designations normally used are "Q" and "T." Of course, there are other variations of transistors, and these are discussed later in this Chapter.

As shown by the symbols, the NPN transistor emitter arrow points away from the base junction while the PNP arrow points toward the base. This is the way all PN and NP junctions are designated. It is important that you remember these symbols when working with solid-state circuits because the bias volt-

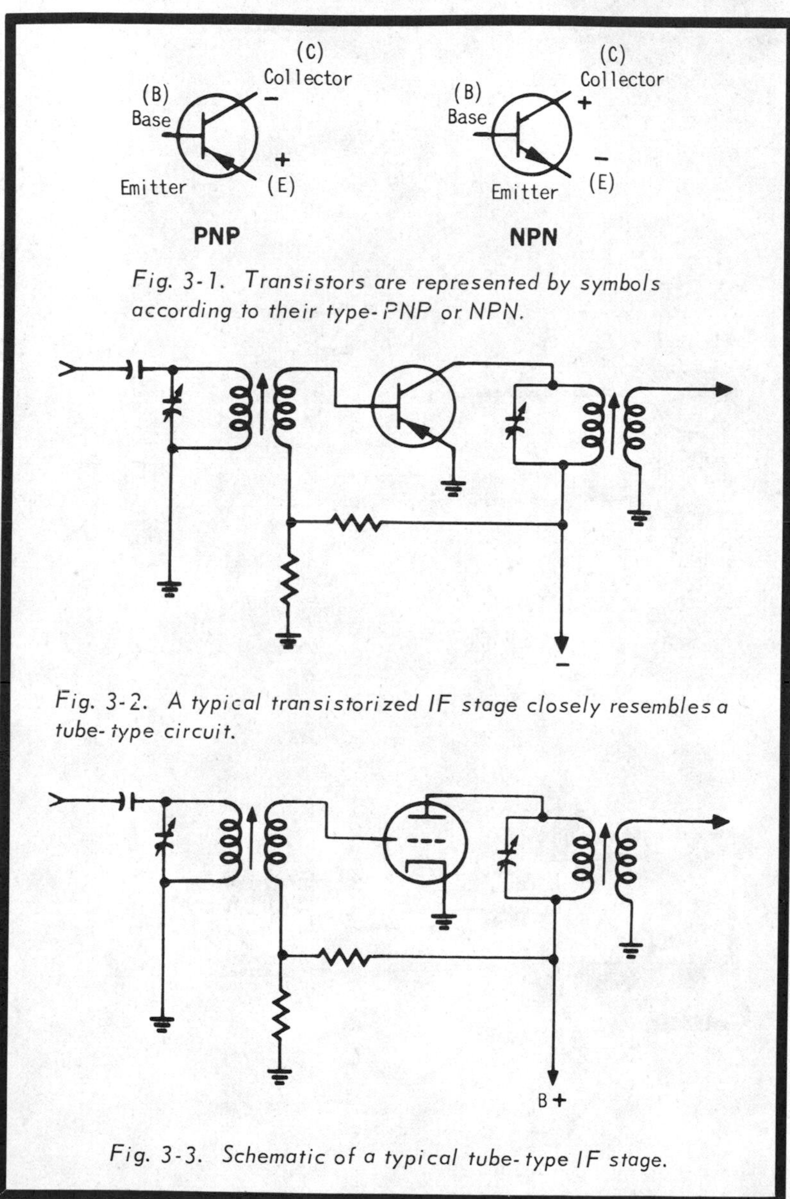


*Fig. 3-1. Transistors are represented by symbols according to their type- PNP or NPN.*

*Fig. 3-2. A typical transistorized IF stage closely resembles a tube-type circuit.*

*Fig. 3-3. Schematic of a typical tube-type IF stage.*

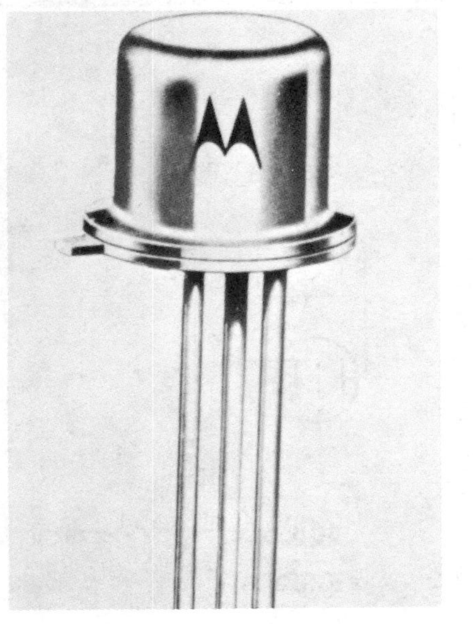

TO- 5 Package

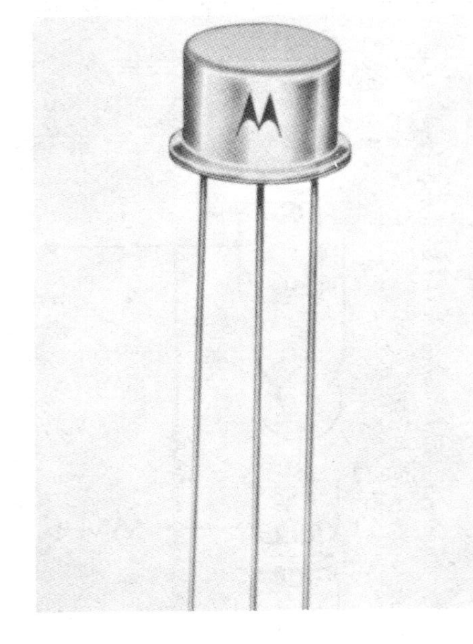

TO- 18 Package

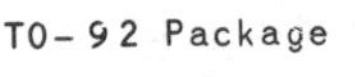

TO- 92 Package

*Fig. 3-4. Typical low-power transistors.*

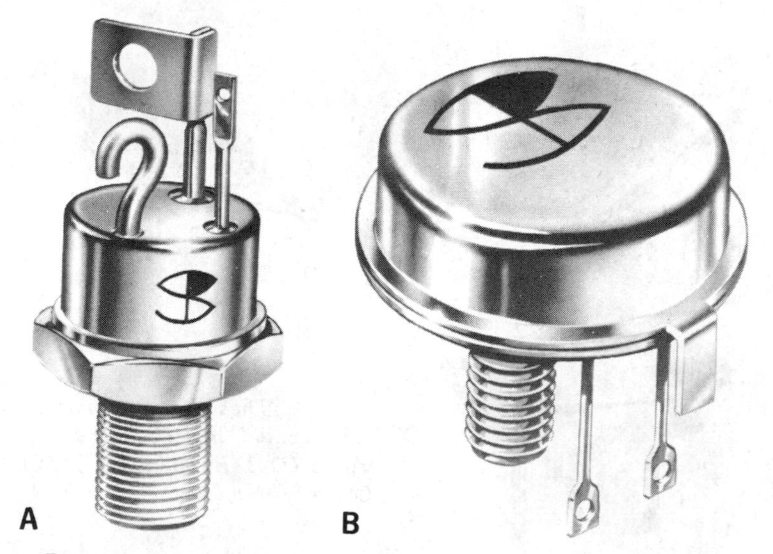


*Fig. 3-5. Typical high-power transistors: the TO-114 case configuration (A) and the TO-82 (B). Courtesy Solid-State Power Corp.*

ages are opposite for the PNP and NPN types and the two cannot be interchanged. In other words, a PNP transistor must be replaced with a PNP.

Transistorized circuits are not too unlike basic tube circuits, except that they are physically much smaller and use lower voltages. Simplified schematics of a transistorized IF stage and an equivalent tube circuit are shown in Figs. 3-2 and 3-3.

Typically, transistors used in low-power circuits are mounted by their leads and have the appearance of the units shown in Fig. 3-4. High-power transistors are physically larger with heavier leads to handle the larger currents (see Fig. 3-5). Transistors of this type are often mounted on a "heat sink," which is nothing more than a metal mounting surface capable of dissipating a greater amount of heat than the transistor case itself.

The physical appearance and size of a transistor is often referred to as its "package" type or "case configuration." "Packages" have been designated with a standardized group of letters and numbers to make physical identification easier. For example, TO-3, TP-16, TO-32. The transistors shown in Fig. 3-5 are designated as TO-114 and TO-82 packages. Fig. 3-6 illustrates several other basic types.

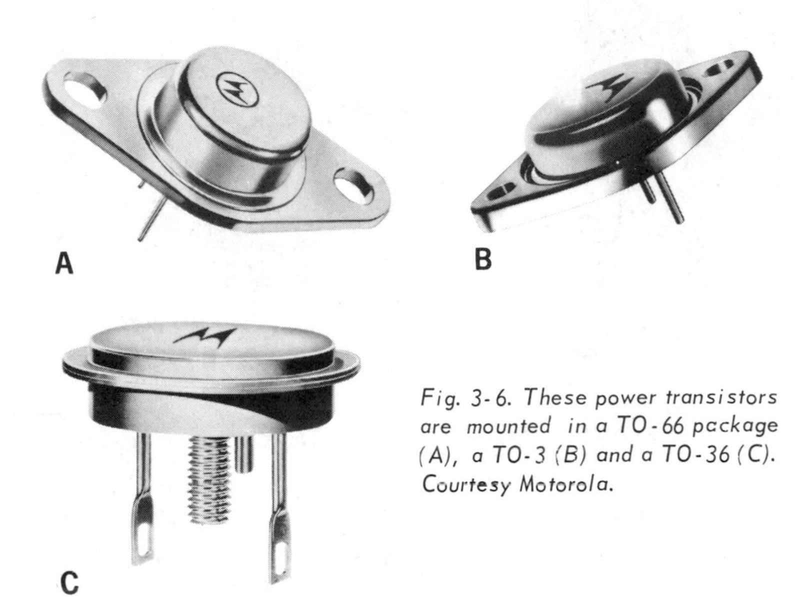


*Fig. 3-6. These power transistors are mounted in a TO-66 package (A), a TO-3 (B) and a TO-36 (C). Courtesy Motorola.*

The types of transistors used in various circuit applications also vary in construction, although they are still PNP or NPN types. By this we mean that a transistor can be made of either germanium or silicon and it can be a junction, epitaxial, mesa, unijunction, or field-effect type. Each has its own operating characteristics for certain applications. Generally, a junction transistor is used as an amplifier. An epitaxial transistor is better for higher power and frequency operation. A mesa transistor is somewhat like the junction but provides better high-frequency gain; it's more rugged and will handle more power. The unijunction and field-effect devices will be discussed later under "special devices."

## DIODES

Solid-state diodes can be described simply as being one-half of a transistor. In other words, a diode can be germanium or silicon with one piece of N-type and one piece of P-type material. The two pieces are joined as in a transistor at a point called the "junction." Also, as in a transistor, the P-type material is considered positive and the N-type, negative.

The schematic symbol for a diode is shown in Fig. 3-7. The most common letter designation is "CR"; however, the letter

"D" is also used sometimes. As might be expected, there are several special types of diodes such as the zener, tunnel, and photo diodes which are discussed later in this Chapter.

*Fig. 3-7. Schematic symbol for a diode.*

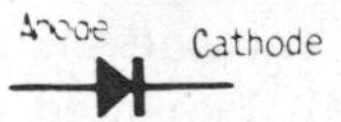


A solid-state diode functions much the same as a diode tube in that it passes current easier in one direction than another. This allows it to function as a rectifier. In other words, a diode is a unilateral device. In a diode, the P-type material is considered to be the anode and as you recall the P-type material is positive. So in a diode, the current flow is from negative (N-type) to positive (P-type). Referring to the schematic symbol, the anode is the arrow of the diode so current flow then will be <u>against</u> the arrow. This is also the direction of least resistance. A good diode when measured with an ohmmeter will have a front-to-back ratio of several hundred ohms.

*Fig. 3-8. Typical diodes— low-current types (A, B) and a high-current stud-mounted diode (C). Courtesy Motorola.*

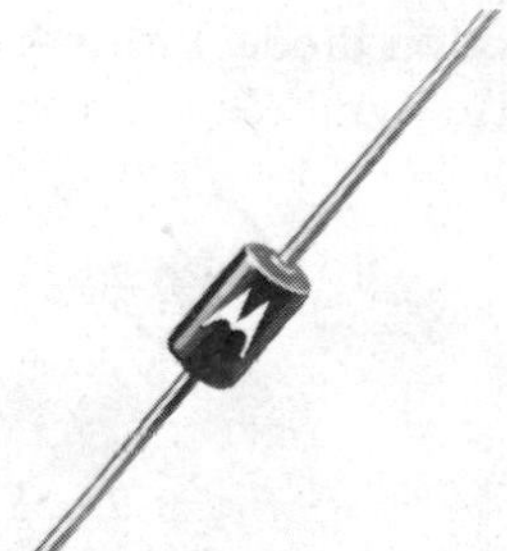

A

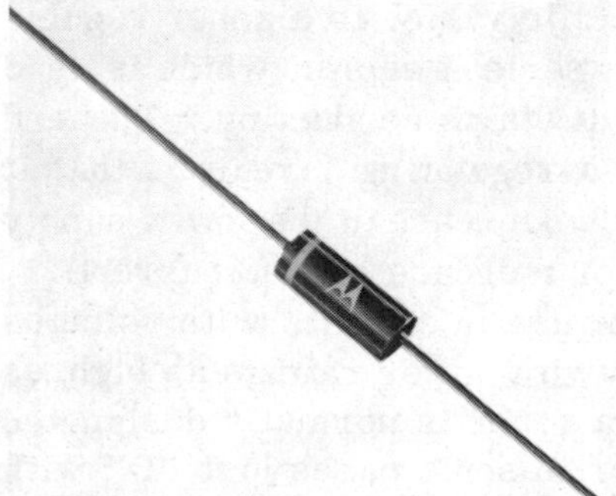

B

C

This means it should measure a greater resistance in one direction than in the other. If the reading is low both ways, chances are it is shorted.

The diode itself is always marked in some way to designate the cathode end. Polarity may be shown by the actual diode symbol printed on the body, or it may be a dot or a colored strip. Examples of various diodes are shown in Fig. 3-8.

Solid-state diodes, just as transistors, are made for specific applications. Those used in low-power circuits are physically smaller than devices used in large current applications. Some mount by their axial leads while others have heavy studs designed for heat dissipation.

## ZENER DIODES

A zener or zener diode is a special device used primarily for holding a voltage within a given limit. Zener diodes are also sometimes referred to as backward diodes and voltage-regulator diodes. A zener is similar in operation to a silicon junction diode with reverse bias and basically the same schematic symbols are used as shown in Fig. 3-9.

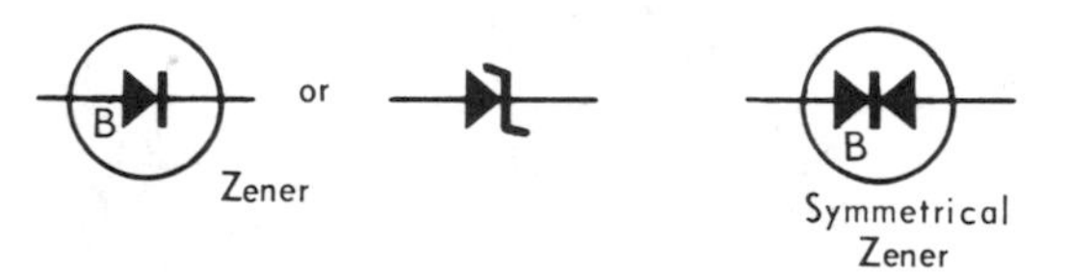


*Fig. 3-9. Special symbols are often used to indicate a zener diode.*

The zener maintains a fixed voltage because it conducts when the reverse bias reaches a specific value. In a zener regulating circuit, there is always a series resistor which is used to limit the diode current once it starts conducting. The end result of zener conduction in a regulating circuit is that it compensates for any increase or decrease in the power supply voltage (caused by a decrease or increase of load current).

Zener diodes are available for use in circuits with voltages ranging from 2.4 to 200, and with power ratings as high as 50 watts. On the schematic, a zener is normally designated by the letters "ZD," "ZR," or in some cases just "D" with the schematic symbol and parts list indicating that it is a zener. Because of the zener's small size, long life, and wide selection of available operating voltages, it has gained tremendous popularity in electronic equipment—especially when stability is necessary.

## TUNNEL DIODES

The tunnel diode, or the Esaki diode, as it is sometimes called, is shown schematically in Fig. 3-10. It has some very special features which make it a popular device for low-power, high-frequency applications.

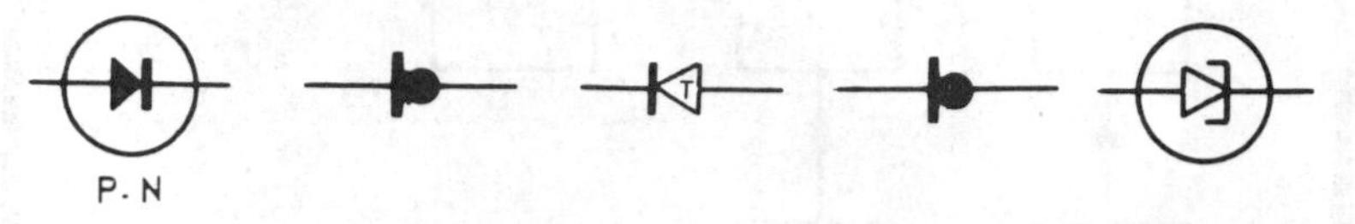


*Fig. 3-10. Any of these symbols indicate a tunnel used in the circuit.*

The name "tunnel" comes from the way electrical charges go through the junction barrier on one side of the diode; they seem to disappear while another charge suddenly "pops" out on the other side. This happens at the speed of light. Some of the important features of this device are that it can operate at higher temperatures than silicon or germanium diodes and at frequencies as high as 10 GHz. Tunnel diodes can be made extremely small in size.

## VARACTOR DIODES

Varactor diodes employ a condition which exists at a PN-junction diode when reverse bias is applied, a condition that makes the diode act like a capacitor. Schematic symbols for a varactor diode are shown in Fig. 3-11.

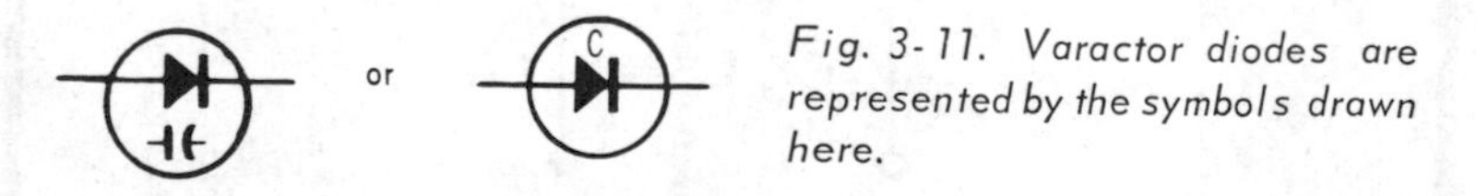


*Fig. 3-11. Varactor diodes are represented by the symbols drawn here.*

As you may recall, a capacitor is made of two plates separated by an insulating material. The barrier region at the PN junction of a diode acts just like a capacitor when it is reversed biased. The actual reason why the PN junction acts like a capacitor is quite involved, but simply think of each side

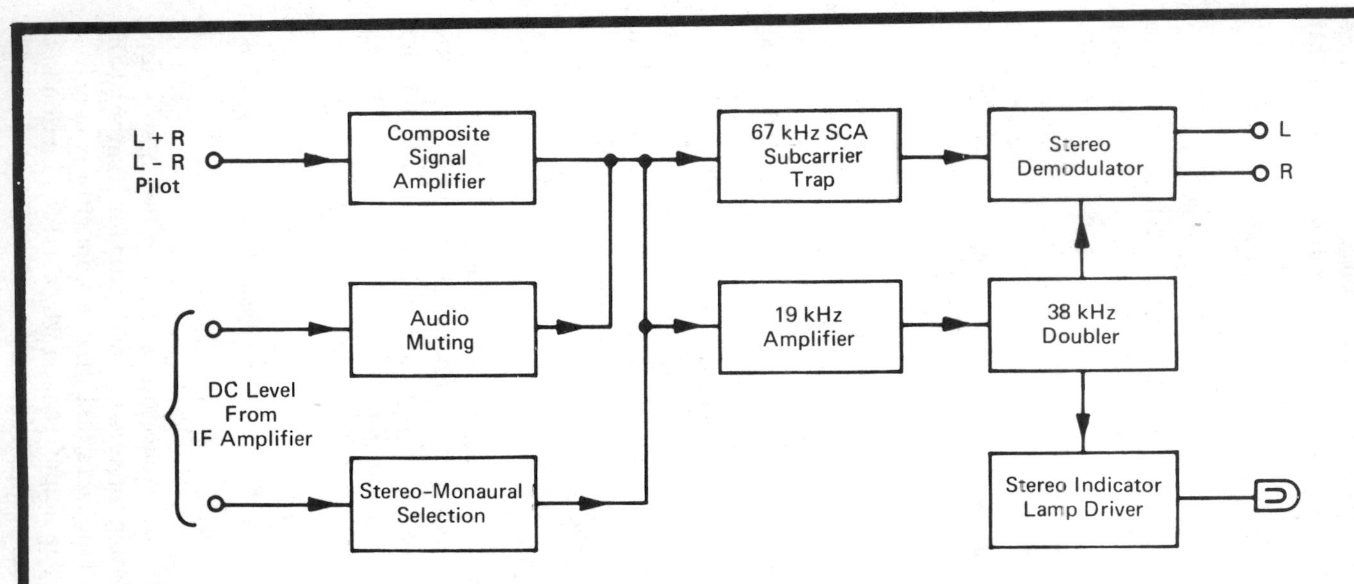


*Fig. 3-12. Block diagram of an integrated circuit (IC) FM stereo demodulator. The IC contains the equivalent of 30 transistors, 10 diodes, and 27 resistors! Courtesy Motorola.*

of the junction as the plates of a capacitor. As the bias voltage varies, the spacing between the plates varies and so does the capacitance. Varactor diodes are made to take advantage of this and they have recently become very popular in oscillator tuning circuits.

## INTEGRATED CIRCUITS

Have you ever wondered what kind of devices it takes to build a pocket-sized TV set, a receiver smaller than a postage stamp, or a complete audio amplifier in less space than a period at the end of a sentence? Obviously it calls for miniature components, or more specifically, integrated circuits. An integrated circuit—or IC—is single "component" containing resistors, capacitors, diodes, and transistors on a single, tiny clip. The block diagram in Fig. 3-12 illustrates the large number of stages which can be built into just one of these devices. Fig. 3-13 shows two common case designs.

ICs, besides being micro-miniature in size, have high reliability characteristics and can be mass produced, resulting in lower cost They are becoming increasingly popular in home entertainment products such as hi-fi amplifiers, FM, and television receivers. An example of IC application in a stereo amplifier is shown in Fig. 3-14. However, the largest uses for ICs are still in the space and computer fields.

The manufacture of an integrated circuit requires a great many steps. Briefly, an IC starts as a thin slice of silicon with the circuit elements built up on it as layers of doped semiconductor material and silicon dioxide in a number of steps. It is completed by adding the connecting leads. Manufacturing processes are continually being perfected to reduce production costs and increase IC popularity.

Integrated circuits are normally soldered into a circuit just like transistors, except there are many more leads. Packaging is one of the biggest considerations in IC technology. Many currently used in consumer products are designed for ease of replacement since ICs themselves are not made to be repaired. Working on and around ICs requires the same careful attention given any solid-state device.

## SPECIAL DEVICES

SCR (Silicon Controlled Rectifier): The silicon controlled rectifier is identified by the schematic symbol shown in Fig.

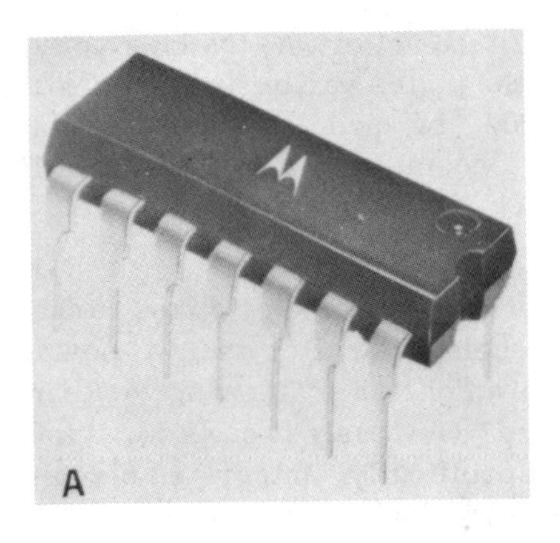

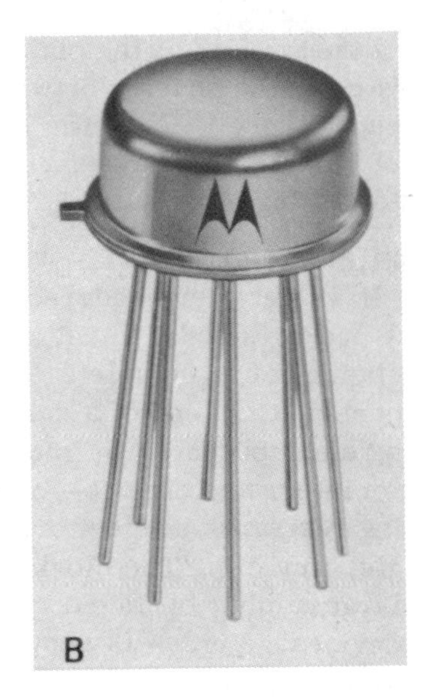

*Fig. 3-13. Like transistors ICs are housed in various case types—dual in-line (A) and metal (B). Courtesy Motorola.*

3-15. It is designed for high power applications such as rectifying, regulation, and switching in motor speed control and light dimming circuits, for example. A SCR can be compared to a switch since it acts something like a diode. That is, when an SCR is operating, its resistance or impedance to current flow is very low. When an SCR is turned off, its impedance is very high.

As shown in Fig. 3-15, the SCR has three terminals labeled anode, cathode, and gate. When connected to a circuit, a positive signal applied to the gate terminal is used to switch the SCR on. Once it is switched on, it can be shut off only by lowering its anode voltage to a specific level. The anode and

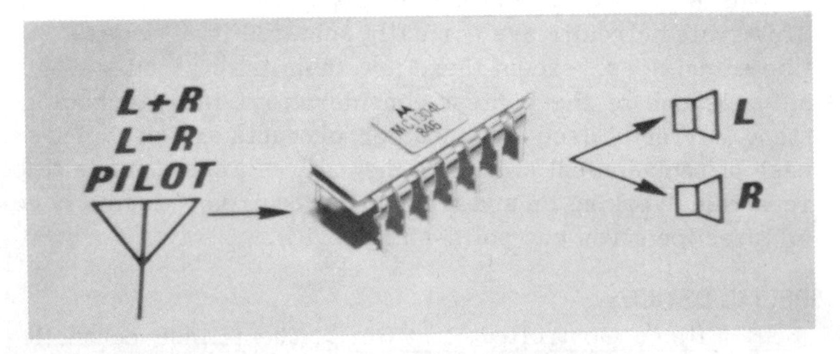


*Fig. 3-14. In-line IC designed to function as an FM stereo demodulator.*

cathode operate the same as their counterparts in a normal diode rectifier. Like other members of the semiconductor family, the SCR comes in many shapes and sizes, depending on the circuit requirements.

SCS (Silicon Controlled Switch): This device is similar to the SCR, except as shown in the schematic symbol in Fig. 3-16 it

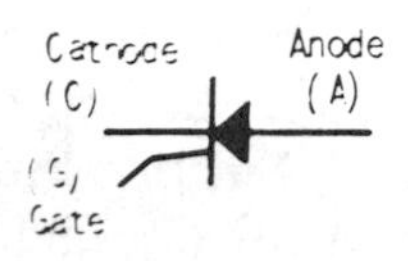


*Fig. 3-15. Silicon controlled rectifiers (SCR) symbol.*

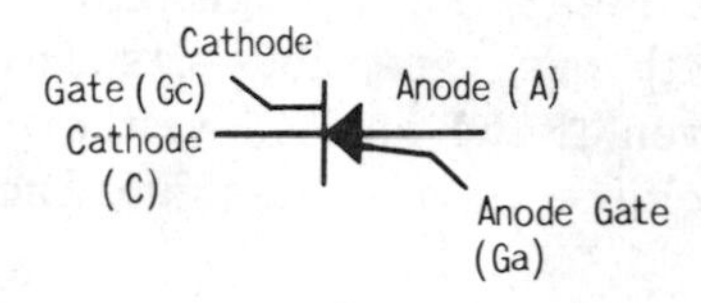


*Fig. 3-16. Silicon controlled switch (SCS) symbol.*

*Fig. 3-17. Symbol for a diac.*

has two gate terminals instead of one. The SCS operates at lower currents and requires a negative gate signal to turn it on rather than positive.

Diac: The diac looks like two diodes in parallel as shown in the schematic symbol in Fig. 3-17. The name itself suggests a dual function which is pretty close to the explanation of the way this device works.

The diac will conduct regardless of the polarity of the applied voltage. As voltage is applied, one half of the diac is turned on as the proper level or "breakdown voltage" is exceeded. The other half is biased off. Then, if the input polarity is switched, the opposite half of the diac will conduct while the previously conducting half is turned off.

Diacs can be used as relaxation oscillators, but they tend to stay in conduction when the input signal voltage goes much over 50 Hz, so their effective operation is restricted to low-frequency applications.

Triac: A triac is a unique device something like an SCR since it is also used in controlled circuits. It even operates like an SCR in that it can handle large currents and can be switched on through the gate. As the schematic symbol in Fig. 3-18 illustrates, the triac looks like a diac with the addition of a gate terminal. In fact, it operates on either voltage polarity like a diac. But like the diac and SCR, it is effective only at low frequencies (around 50 Hz).

In reference to diacs, we said that one half of a diac conducts when its "breakdown voltage" is exceeded, while the other side is biased off as this condition reverses when the polarity of the applied voltage reverses. A triac works the same way with one exception—its gate circuit allows it to be turned on even if the applied voltage does not reach the "breakdown voltage" level. The gate then acts like a switch.

## FIELD-EFFECT TRANSISTORS (FET)

The field-effect transistor today is available in two types. One is called the "junction field-effect transistor" which is now commonly known as simply the field-effect transistor or

*Fig. 3-18. The triac symbol shows the addition of a control element to a diac symbol.*

FET. The second is the "insulated-gate field-effect transsistor" or IGFET. This device is also referred to as the MOSFET or metal-oxide semiconductor. The IGFET, or MOSFET, is described later.

The FET is very similar in operation to a vacuum tube. Its main feature is that it is a very high-impedance device. Because of this, it is popular for input circuits in voltmeters and other measuring instruments where minimum circuit loading is desired. An ordinary voltmeter, or one that is not a high-impedance type, may cause a change in the circuit being measured and result in inaccurate readings. High input impedance devices such as the FET prevent this.

The schematic symbol for an FET is shown in Fig. 3-19. Like a transistor, it can be either an NPN or PNP type. Its terminals, labeled gate, drain, and source, are comparable to the grid, plate, and cathode of a vacuum tube. The source and drain terminals are connected to opposite ends of a piece of N-type material. Current will flow from source to drain

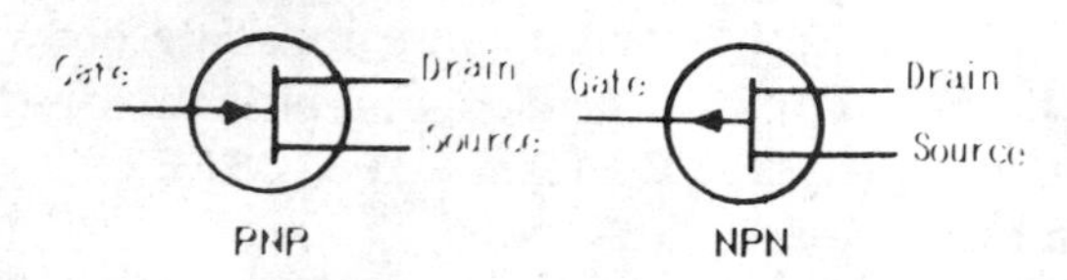


*Fig. 3-19. FETs are represented with this symbol.*

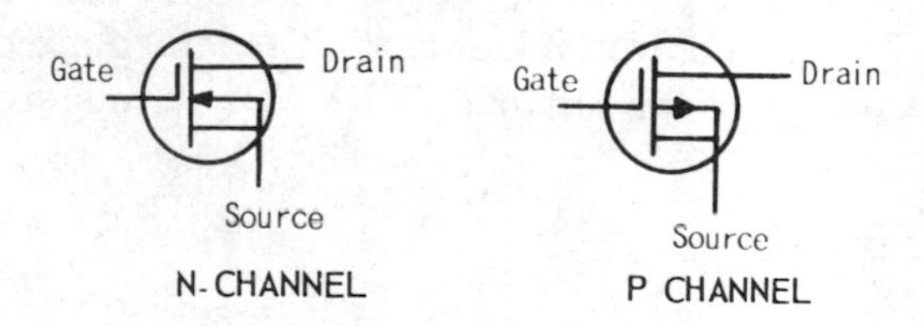


*Fig. 3-20. Symbols for IGFETs and MOSFETs.*

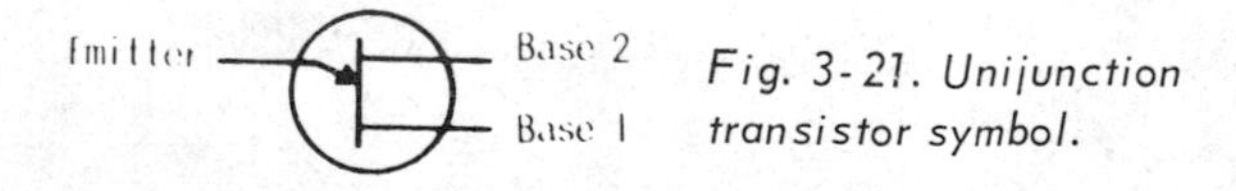


*Fig. 3-21. Unijunction transistor symbol.*

when the proper voltage is applied and with no voltage applied between the gate and source. As in the grid circuit of a vacuum tube, when voltage is applied between the gate (grid) terminal and the source (cathode) terminal, it will regulate current flow.

## Igfets & Mos-Fets

The insulated-gate field-effect transistor (IGFET) is similar to the FET except that as the name says, its gate is insulated by a material called the "substrate." For this reason, its impedance characteristics are better than the FET.

Like the FET, an IGFET can be either an NPN or PNP type as shown in Fig. 3-20. It is an effective device in the input circuits of test instruments and audio applications where high impedance is desirable. The IGFET or MOSFET requires careful handling because of the high-impedance characteristic. The static electricity in a person's body is enough to damage them. For this reason, manufacturers normally caution users to handle IGFETs and MOSFETs by the case rather than by the leads.

## UNIJUNCTION TRANSISTOR

The unijunction transistor is shown schematically in Fig. 3-21. It looks like an FET but actually operates more like a tunnel diode. The UJI is basically a low-frequency switching device used in timing circuits, voltage comparators, relaxation oscillators, and for triggering SCRs in control applications. Its physical appearance is like any transistor.

## CHAPTER 4

# Vacuum Tubes

Vacuum tubes are used in various electronic equipment and will continue to be for many years, even though transistors are now replacing them in most applications. The reason is that there are still many functions and designs for which entirely suitable solid-state devices have yet to be perfected.

Tubes, of course, are available in a great many types and styles for various circuit functions, but they all have certain common characteristics. The electrodes or elements of a tube are housed in a glass or metal envelope which has been evacuated by drawing out all the gases. The most basic tube is the diode, so called because it has only two elements—a cathode which emits electrons and a plate or anode which collects the electrons. All tubes have at least these two elements.

The common schematic letter designation for tubes is the letter "V," such as V2, V6, etc. Dual tubes, such as a dual-diode or dual-triode, are usually indentified in two sections such as V2A and V2B or V6A and V6B. (More on dual tubes later.)

In some tubes, the cathode and filament are the same element. Such tubes have directly-heated cathodes. Other tubes have indirectly-heated cathodes in which a separate cathode is heated by a filament. The two types are shown in Fig. 4-1. The cathode, whether directly or indirectly heated, emits electrons into the vacuum. When the anode or plate is made positive with respect to the cathode, it will attract these electrons, resulting in current flow.

Since electrons must travel from the cathode to plate, other elements can be added in between to control this current flow. Thus a third element—called a "control grid"—is introduced and it is capable of exerting significant influence over the electron stream from cathode to plate. Some tubes have more than one grid—two, three, and in some cases, more. The tube number indicates the number of elements. For example, the triode has three elements, the tetrode has four, and so on.

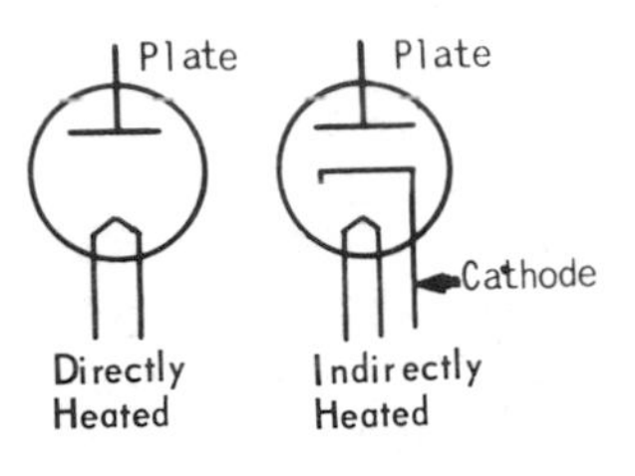


*Fig. 4-1. All vacuum tubes have an electron emitter – called the cathode. In some tubes the heated filament is the emitter; in others the filament merely heats the cathode.*

## DIODES

The two-element tube is a diode. It's schematic symbol is shown in Fig. 4-2. The diode is most often used as a rectifier in power supply circuits. Since current flow in a diode will exist only when the plate is positive with respect to the cathode, an AC signal applied between the plate and cathode results in a current flow only during positive cycles.

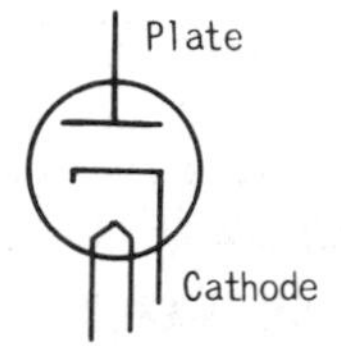


*Fig. 4-2. Schematic symbol for a diode – a two-element tube.*

A diode used in this application is termed a half-wave rectifier because it conducts on only one half of the AC wave. A full-wave rectifier will provide output on both portions of the AC signal if two diodes are connected as shown in Fig. 4-3. A full-wave rectifier tube is actually two separate diodes in a single envelope. Both plates receive electrons from the same cathode.

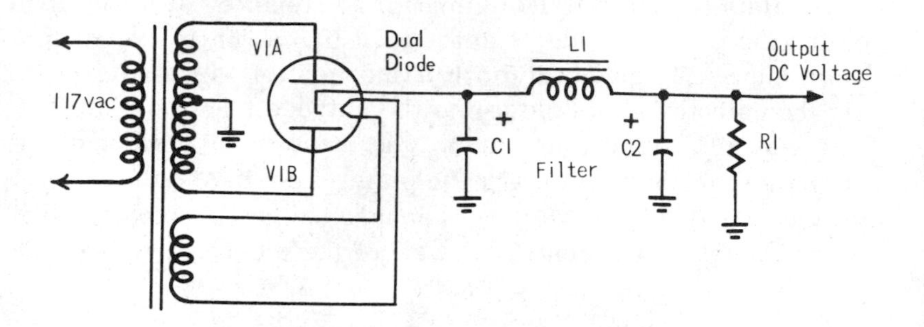


*Fig. 4-3. Full-wave rectifier circuit using a dual-diode tube.*

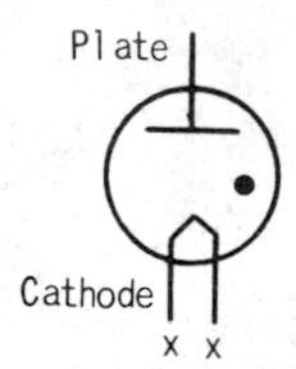


*Fig. 4-4. A gas-filled diode is represented by the symbol shown here.*

Another type of diode commonly used in power supply circuits is the gas-filled diode shown schematically in Fig. 4-4. One of the advantages of a gas diode is more constant output, and it can handle a larger current flow with less power loss.

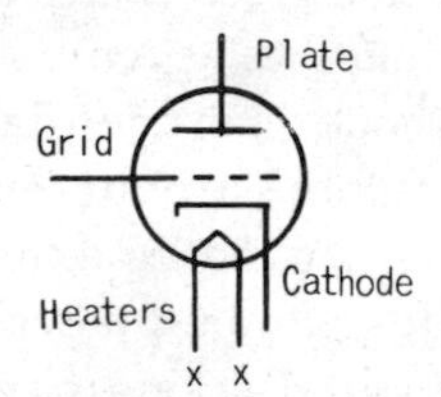


*Fig. 4-5. Adding the third element to the diode we have a triode symbol.*

## TRIODES

The name suggests a three-element tube—a cathode, a control grid, and a plate. The schematic symbol is shown in Fig. 4-5. The grid is placed between the cathode and plate to regulate the current flow through the tube. That's why it is called the control grid. It acts much like a control valve in a water pipe. The grid is actually a fine mesh of wires surrounding the cathode and is closer to the cathode than the plate.

As we said, electrons leave the heated cathode and are attracted to the plate when the plate is positive with respect to the cathode. However, because some space exists between these two elements, not all of the electrons will reach

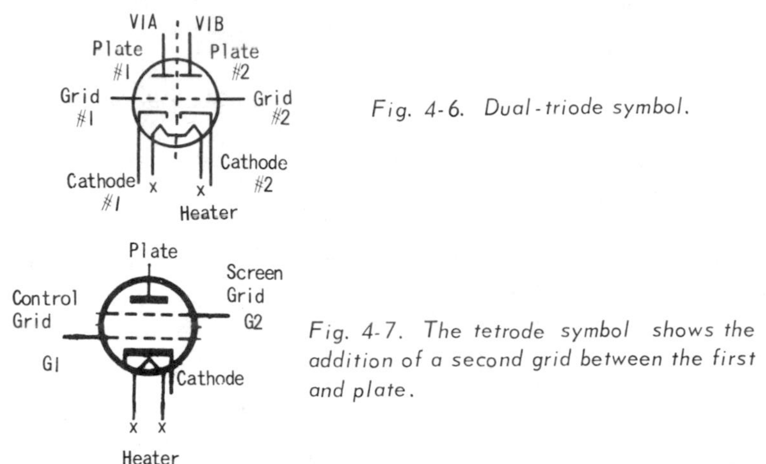


Fig. 4-6. Dual-triode symbol.

Fig. 4-7. The tetrode symbol shows the addition of a second grid between the first and plate.

the plate. Some will collect around the cathode. The more positive the plate, the more electrons it will attract, but this is true only to a point. If a third element, the control grid, is placed close to the cathode and made slightly positive, it will essentially attract more of the electrons crowded around to the grid to cause grid current, but most will be attracted by the more positive plate resulting in a higher tube current. Since the grid is so much closer to the cathode than the plate, a small grid voltage will produce large effects on plate current. Because of this, triodes are commonly used as amplifiers. As in the case of diodes, two triodes can be placed in one envelope. Such a tube is known as a dual triode shown by the schematic symbol in Fig. 4-6.

## TETRODE

The tetrode is a four-element tube having two grids, in addition to the two basic elements (plate and cathode). The tetrode schematic symbol as illustrated in Fig. 4-7 shows the second grid—called a "screen" grid—between the control grid and the plate. The purpose of the screen grid is to reduce the capacitance between the control grid and the plate, a condition which often causes problems during high-frequency operation. The control grid still acts to regulate plate current as it does in the triode, but the control grid's affect is much greater in the terode, making it a higher gain amplifier.

In most circuit applications, the screen grid is bypassed to ground with a capacitor. This effectively places the screen grid at signal ground to further reduce the capacitance between the plate and control grid. The most common application for the tetrode is in amplifier circuits, but the pentode tube is more widely used except in certain applications.

## PENTODE

The pentode tube has five elements—a cathode, plate, control grid, and screen grid, just as in a tetrode, plus one additional element called the "suppressor" grid. The schematic symbol for the pentode is shown in Fig. 4-8.

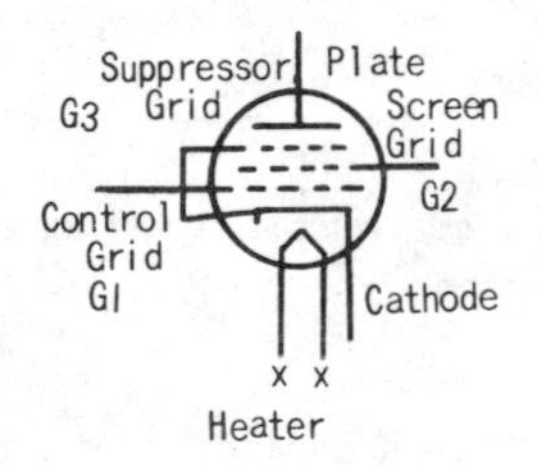


*Fig. 4-8. Adding still another grid to the tetrode symbol and it becomes a pentode.*

In the tetrode, the screen grid was added to reduce the capacitance between the control grid and plate, resulting in better amplification at higher frequencies. However, during conduction, electrons hitting the plate cause some electrons to be knocked off, producing an effect known as "secondary emission." This "secondary" electron flow occurs when the electrons knocked off the plate are attracted by the screen grid which results in distortion and unwanted oscillations. To eliminate this effect, a suppressor grid was placed between the screen grid and plate. As shown in the pentode symbol (Fig. 4-8), the suppressor grid is tied to the cathode. This means it is negative with respect to the plate and, therefore, it repells secondary emissions from the plate.

The pentode has a much higher amplification factor than either the triode or tetrode and is used in amplifier stages where high gain and high plate resistance is desirable.

## BEAM POWER TUBES

A beam power tube can be either a tetrode or pentode. The "beam" power characteristic comes from the fact that the electron stream from the cathode to the plate is formed into a narrow beam by special plates. In effect, these plates concentrate the flow of electrons much like funneling the water from a large pipe through a narrow nozzle. The pressure or force is much greater.

This concentration or beam does two things: it allows the tube to produce higher output power and it reduces secondary emission. The reason it produces greater power is that more electrons reach the plate faster than in an ordinary tetrode or pentode. Secondary emission, as mentioned earlier, is caused by electrons hitting the plate and knocking other electrons back. That's why a suppressor grid was put in the pentode,

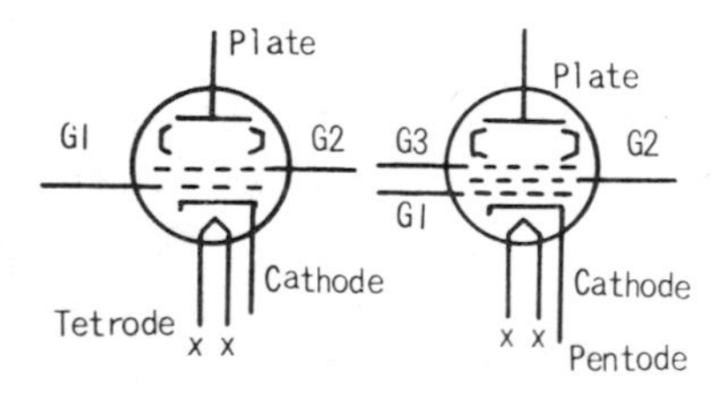


*Fig. 4-9. These symbols represent beam power tubes.*

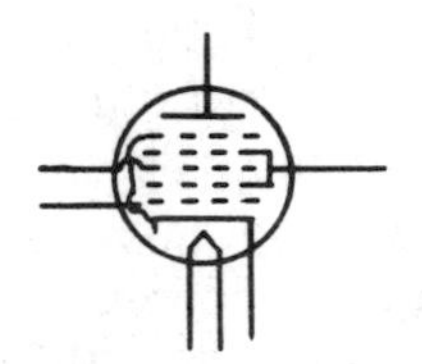

*Fig. 4-10. Five-grid tube, appropriately called a "pentagrid" was designed for converter circuits.*

to repel this action. However, since the electrons in a beam power tube are so concentrated, those that are knocked off the plate are turned right back. It would be like trying to swim against a heavy current. The schematic symbols for beam power tubes are shown in Fig. 4-9.

## PENTAGRID TUBES

As the heading suggests, the pentagrid tube has five grids as shown by the schematic symbol in Fig. 4-10. It is considered a multi-unit type because in actual use it combines the functions of more than one tube. For instance, the pentagrid is often used as an oscillator and a mixer in superheterodgne receiver circuits. A pentagrid tube serving these functions is commonly referred to as a "pentagrid converter."

A simplified schematic of a typical oscillator mixer circuit using the pentagrid converter is shown in Fig. 4-11. In this circuit, the cathode, control grid, and screen grid (grids 2 and 4) act as the oscillator section. The incoming signal is mixed with the oscillator signal also present in the tube. Pentagrid converter circuits are common in AC-DC and battery-operated units, including automobile broadcast receivers. It is also sometimes used as a "product" detector in single sideband receivers.

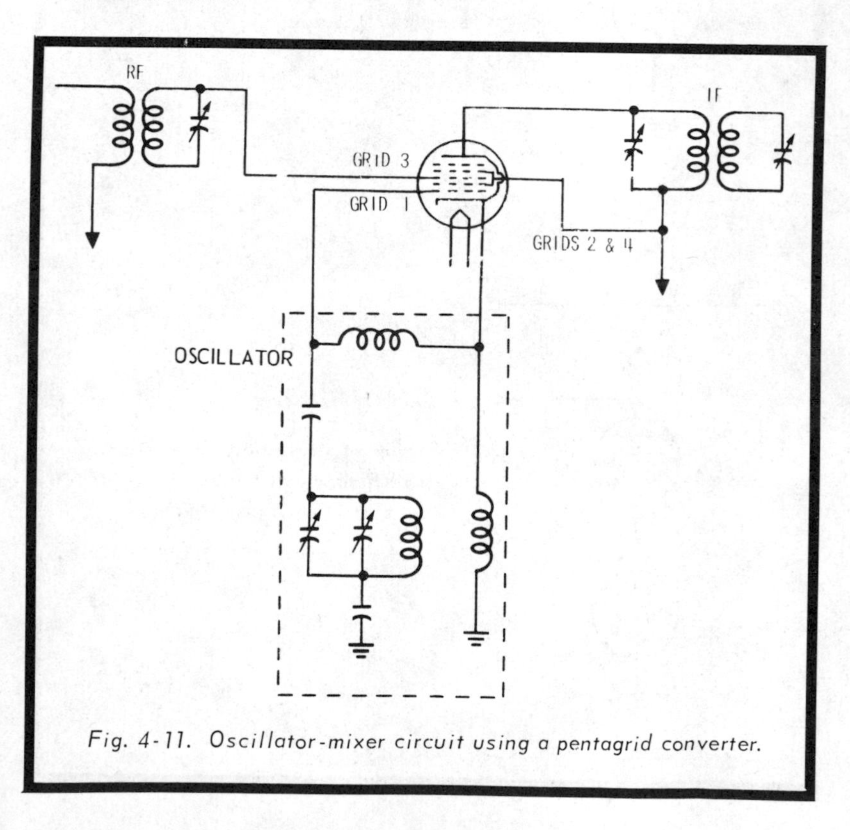


*Fig. 4-11. Oscillator-mixer circuit using a pentagrid converter.*

*Fig. 4-12. Schematic symbol used for gaseous regulator tubes.*

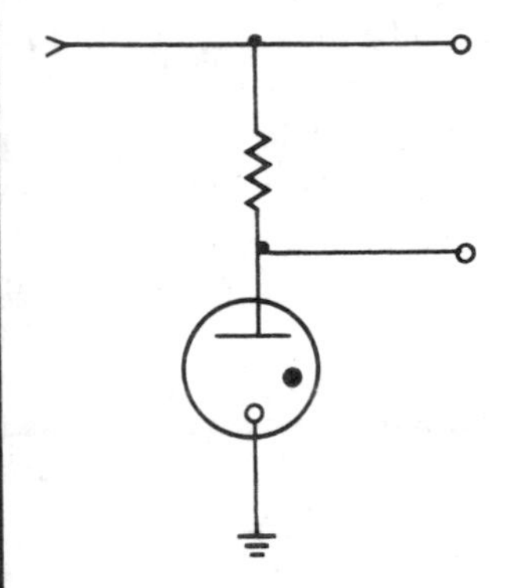

*Fig. 4-13. Regulator circuit using a single VR tube.*

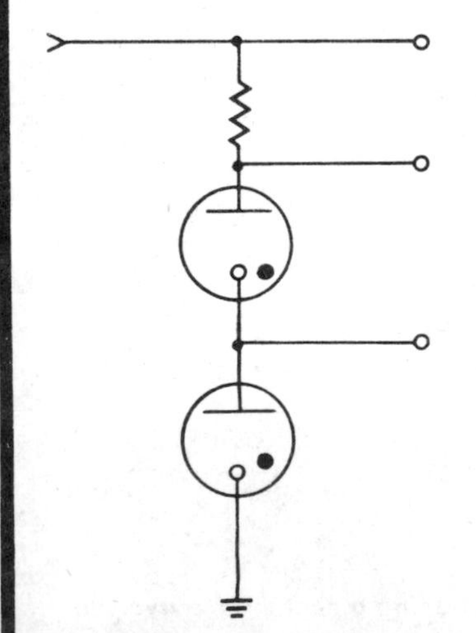

*Fig. 4-14. Regulator circuit using two VR tubes in series.*

## REGULATOR TUBES

Regulator tubes are used to maintain a constant power supply voltage regardless of load variations. In this respect, they serve the same purpose as zener diodes discussed earlier. The regulator is a gas-filled tube such as an OB2/VR105 or an OA2/VR150, and they can be obtained to regulate voltages at 75, 90, 105, and 150 volts. The gaseous regulator tube, sometimes referred to as the "VR" tube, is shown schematically in Fig. 4-12 and is designated by the letters VR.

Typical circuit applications are illustrated in Figs. 4-13 and 4-14. The gaseous regulator in these circuits has a series limiting resistor just as that used with a zener diode. The resistor value is selected to hold the tube current flow between specific levels. For most regulators, the minimum and maximum current values are between 5 and 40 ma. The voltage regulation capability of a gaseous tube is fairly good as long as the load current does not vary more than 30 ma. In other words, if the normal load current is 75 ma, the most it could vary for good regulation is from 60 to 90 ma (15 ma lower and 15 ma higher, or 30 ma overall). The regulated voltage output is always present across the tube as indicated.

## CATHODE-RAY TUBES

The cathode-ray tube is probably the one most of us see more often than any other because that's exactly what a TV picture tube is. The TV picture we see is actually formed by a beam of electrons which is swept back and forth across the screen to "paint" the image. Naturally, there is a lot more to it than that, but the basic principle is the same for any cathode ray tube, or CRT as it is often called.

CRTs come in two basic types: with electrostatic deflection or magnetic deflection. Both are shown in Figs. 4-15 and 4-16. As indicated, the electrostatic type has deflection plates within the tube itself while an external deflection "yoke" is needed for CRTs designed for magnetic deflection. In both units, the purpose is the same: to sweep the electron beam from the tube gun back and forth across the screen in step with the input signals to produce the correct image.

Both CRT types are found in television sets, oscilloscope

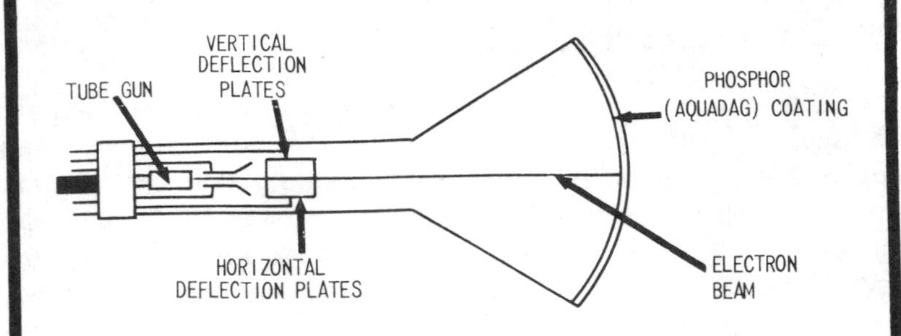


*Fig. 4-15. Symbol for a cathode-ray tube designed for electrostatic deflection.*

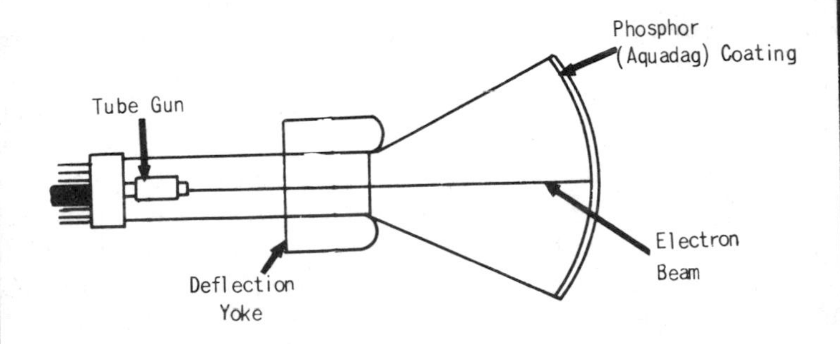


*Fig. 4-16. Without internal plates, this symbol depicts a CRT requiring an external magnetic yoke.*

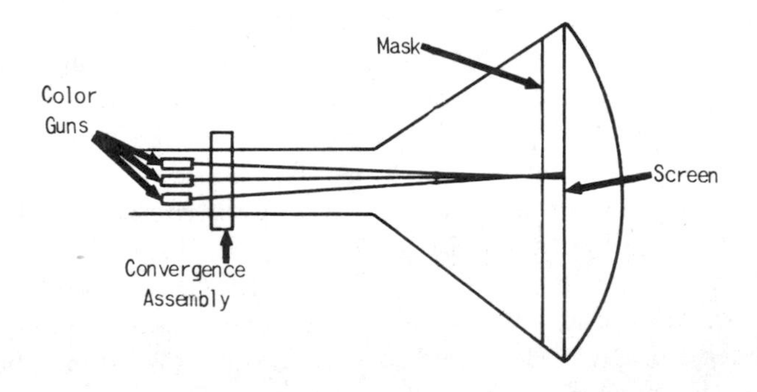


*Fig. 4-17. Schematic symbol of a 3-gun color CRT.*

test instruments, and radar units. Magnetic deflection type cathode-ray tubes are more commonly used in today's home television receiver. The schematic symbol for a cathode ray tube is much like any other tube. A CRT has a filament, cathode, grids, and a plate, as shown in Fig. 4-17. However, the plate is the phosphor coating on the inside of the tube faceplate and the voltage is on the order of thousands of volts compared to the few hundred volts in other types of tubes. The high voltage attracts the electron beam and speeds it past the anode to the phosphor-coated face which glows under bombardment by the electron beam.

Color CRTs operate like the normal B & W type in that an electron beam is swept back and forth in synchronzation with input signals to form images. But a color TV tube has three guns instead of one and the picture tube voltage is twice as high. The three guns which are controlled by the primary colors—red, green, and blue—produce three separate electron beams adjusted to pass through a special mask on the inside of the tube face. And when correctly adjusted, the three electron beams converge at the same spot on the screen to produce a white dot. Varying levels of each primary color are thus mixed to produce the spectrum needed to reproduce transmitted color signals.

CHAPTER 5

# Interconnecting Devices

Now, with an idea of the many types of components that go into making a radio, TV, or stereo, the next question is how are they all connected to form a circuit? In some electronic equipment, mostly large devices and older units, terminal strips, tube sockets, and plugs, function as circuit connection points. Components are then soldered to the various terminal strips, sockets, etc., and wires are used to tie the required circuit points together.

Another technique is to use printed-circuit boards, on which thin layers of metal foil serve as interconnecting wires and tie points. In small transistor radios, for example, everything including the battery, speaker, tuning control, on-off switch, and volume control, is mounted to the circuit board. Very little actual wire is used. However, in most electronic equipment, some type of interconnecting device is needed to go from one point to another or from unit to unit. For example, if a microphone is to be plugged into a stereo amplifier, a special cable and connector are needed to couple the voice signals to the audio input circuit. Or in larger equipment, wiring or cabling is necessary to connect various sections together.

## PRINTED-CIRCUIT BOARDS

A typical printed-circuit board is shown in Fig. 5-1. Notice that the components and controls are all connected by the printed-circuit foil or "lands" on the board material. The foil or "lands" are etched into the circuit board surface, usually a thin coating of copper, and holes are drilled through the board to allow component lead connections. Components are located on the top of the board (opposite the foil side)

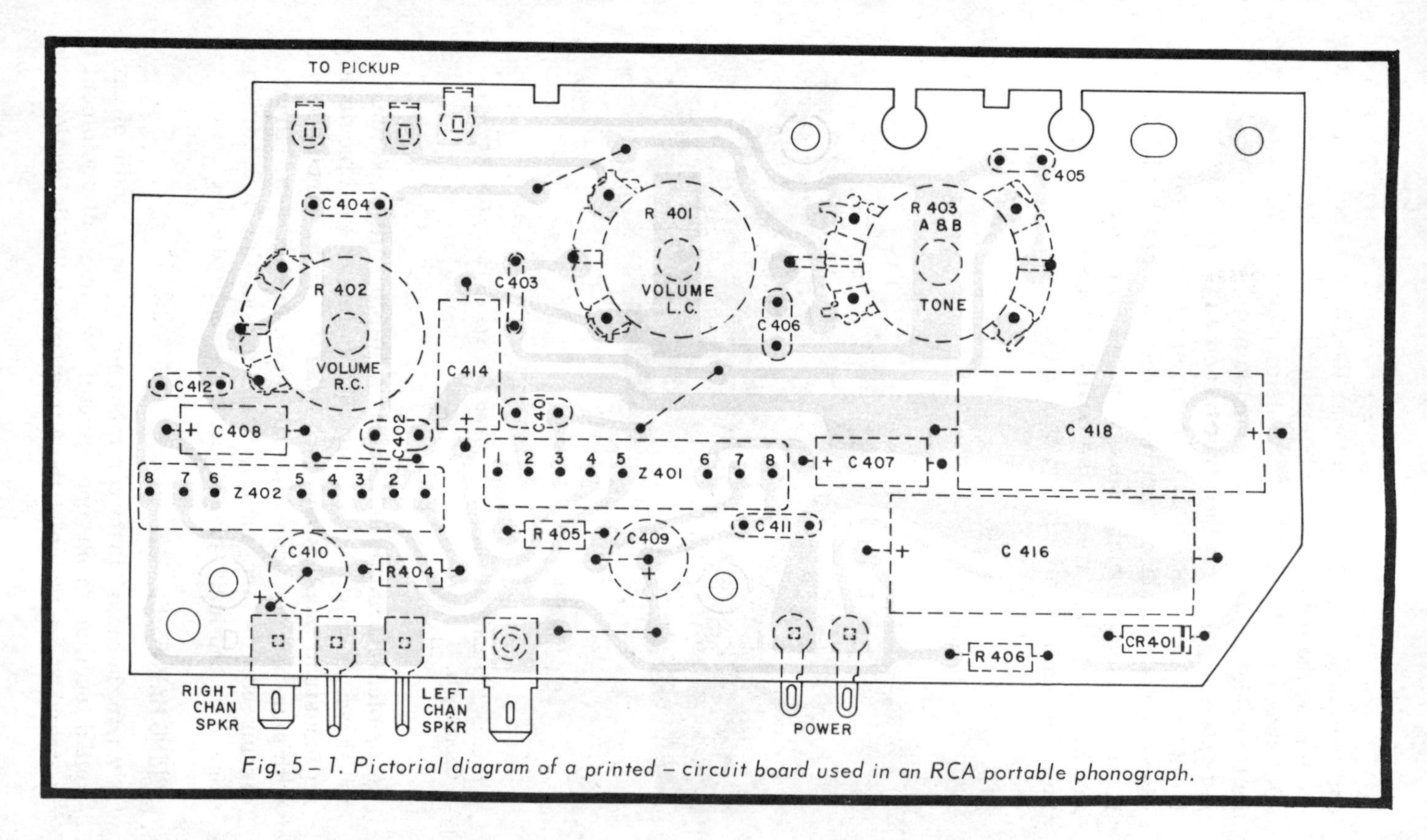


*Fig. 5 – 1. Pictorial diagram of a printed – circuit board used in an RCA portable phonograph.*

and their leads are placed through the holes to be soldered to the foil on the bottom of the board.

As shown in Fig. 5-1, terminals or connectors are conveniently soldered to the circuit board to provide a means of wiring external parts into the circuit such as panel-mounted controls, speakers, etc. In more complicated printed circuits where many connections are required, a special type of connector is used. In such cases all necessary connecting points are brought to one area on the board and a special multi-contact connector is soldered to this area.

*Fig. 5-2. Printed-circuit board used in a stereo multiplex receiver. Courtesy H. H. Scott.*

A printed-circuit board used in a stereo multiplex receiver is shown in Fig. 5-2, along with an integrated circuit (IC). An industrial application requiring multiple circuit boards with plug-in type connectors is shown in Fig. 5-3. Printed-circuit boards are rapidly becoming popular in hundreds of consumer and industrial electronics applications.

## WIRING HARNESSES

"Wiring harness" is the common name given a bundle of wires routed together from one circuit or piece of equipment to another. As an example, the wires from a TV deflection yoke are tied together to form a "harness." The need for wiring harnesses is obvious. It just wouldn't be a neat, safe, economical procedure to have a lot of loose wires running from one area to another.

Wiring harnesses are needed in a number of applications such as from radio to radio in an aircraft, between circuit board assemblies in a computer, from a common power supply to a receiver and transmitter, in a broadcast station from console to transmitter, and many others. In many instances, ready-made harnesses can be purchased with the required number of wires. These are called "cables" and they come in hundreds of variations. The cabling in a telephone installation, for example, may contain as many as 100 wires.

*Fig. 5-3. Plug-in PC boards used in one type of industrial equipment.*

The schematic symbol for multi-conductor cable is shown in Fig. 5-4. In some applications, the entire harness or cable is enclosed in a metal or shielded jacket. The symbol

*Fig. 5-4. Symbol used to signify unshielded multi-conductor cable.*

*Fig. 5-5. This symbol indicates shielded multi-conductor cable.*

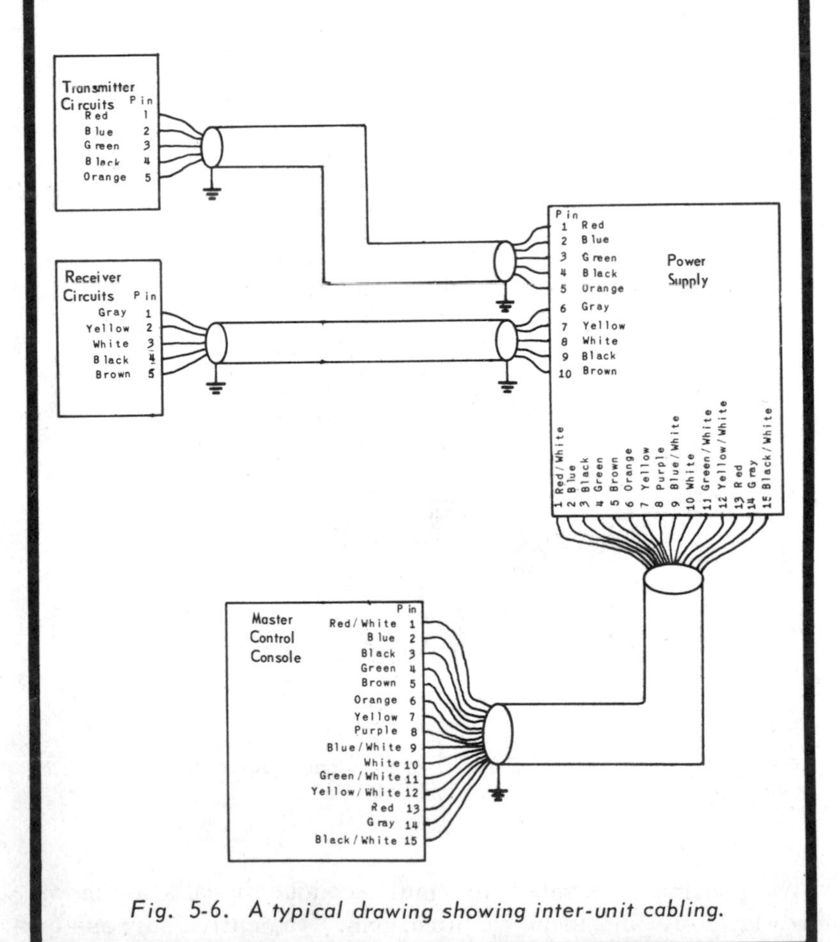


*Fig. 5-6. A typical drawing showing inter-unit cabling.*

for shielded cable is shown in Fig. 5-5. Multi-conductor cables contain color-coded wires to make identification easier when connections are made. The wires may be all the same size or there may be several small and several large diameters for special applications requiring different voltages and currents. Fig. 5-6 is a drawing representing a bundle of wires or multi-conductor cable connecting two circuits or units. Wire identification or coding is necessary for interconnecting cables as indicated, and the coding is also carried on the schematic.

## MULTIPLE-WIRE CONNECTORS

Multiple-wire connectors are used to facilitate electrical connection between circuits and equipment. These connectors may be of almost any type or size depending on the application and number of wires. The connector may be a simple three-wire cable-to-cable type. Or it may be a special connector, designed to handle 100 wires of various sizes, with mechanical locking features to prevent the connectors from accidental separation.

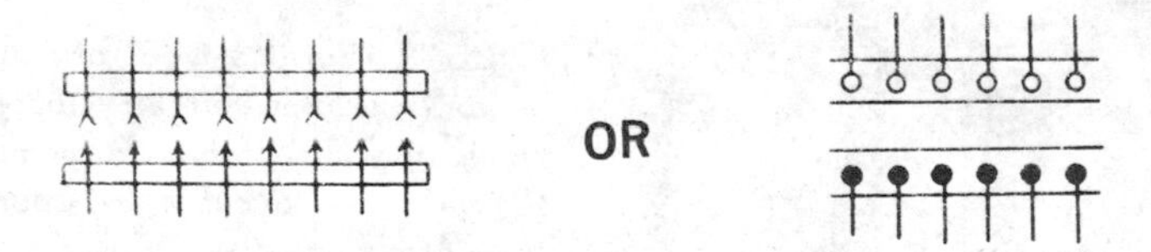


*Fig. 5-7. This type of symbol is used to represent multiple wire connectors. The number of terminals, of course, equals the number of individual conductors in the cable.*

The schematic symbol for a multiple-wire connector is shown in Fig. 5-7. Although the diagram illustrates 6- and 10-pin connectors, the same symbol is used for connectors with more or fewer contacts.

## AUDIO CONNECTORS

An audio-type connector is used to couple audio signals, usually from a source to an amplifier, for example, from a microphone, a turn-table, tape recorder, receiver, or mus-

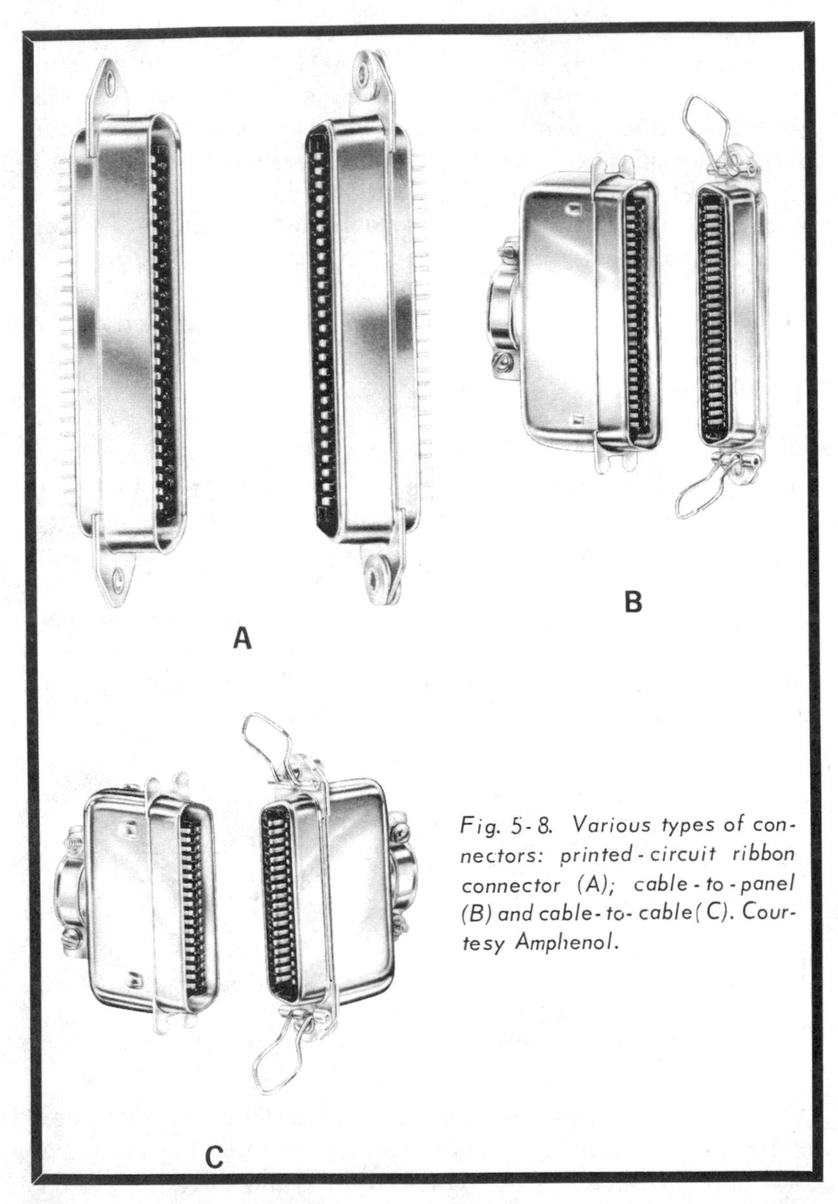


*Fig. 5-8. Various types of connectors: printed-circuit ribbon connector (A); cable-to-panel (B) and cable-to-cable (C). Courtesy Amphenol.*

ical instrument to an amplifier. Audio connectors are designed to transfer the audio signals with as little loss or distortion as possible. The cable used to carry audio signals is always a shielded type and may contain one, two, three, or more wires in addition to the shield. In some cases, each lead has its own shield.

Typical audio connectors are shown in Figs. 5-9 and 5-10. The single-contact type uses one pin for the audio and the case for the shield or ground. Single-wire shielded audio lead is commonly used on musical equipment, turntables, tape recorders, hi fi systems, and on some microphones. A

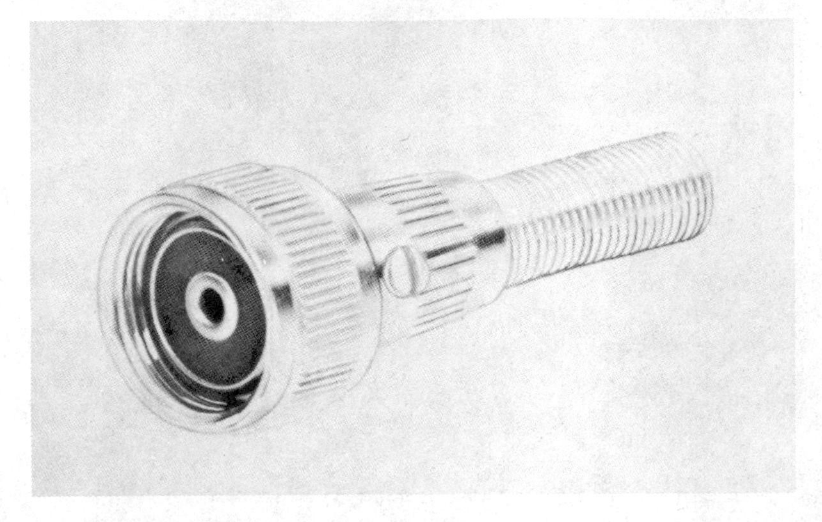

*Fig. 5-9. Popular "75" Series audio connector. Courtesy Amphenol Industrial Div., The Bunker-Ramo Corp.*

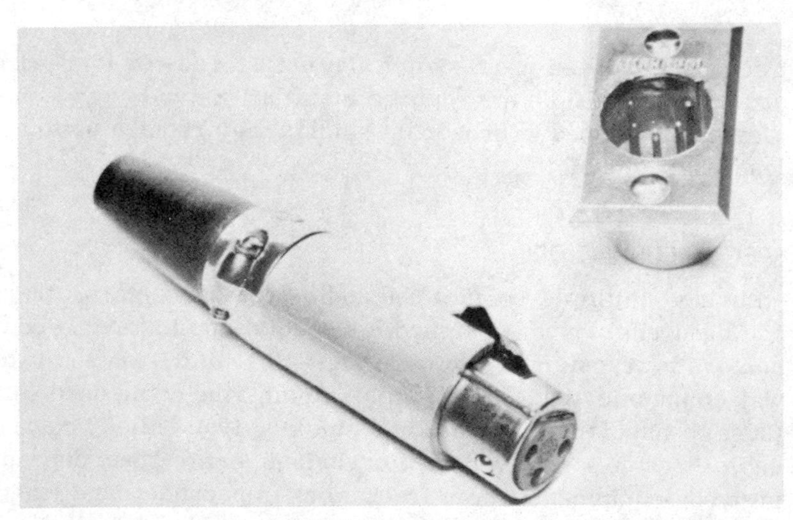

*Fig. 5-10. All-plastic "91" Series quick-disconnect microphone connectors. Courtesy Amphenol Distributor Div., The Bunker-Ramo Corp.*

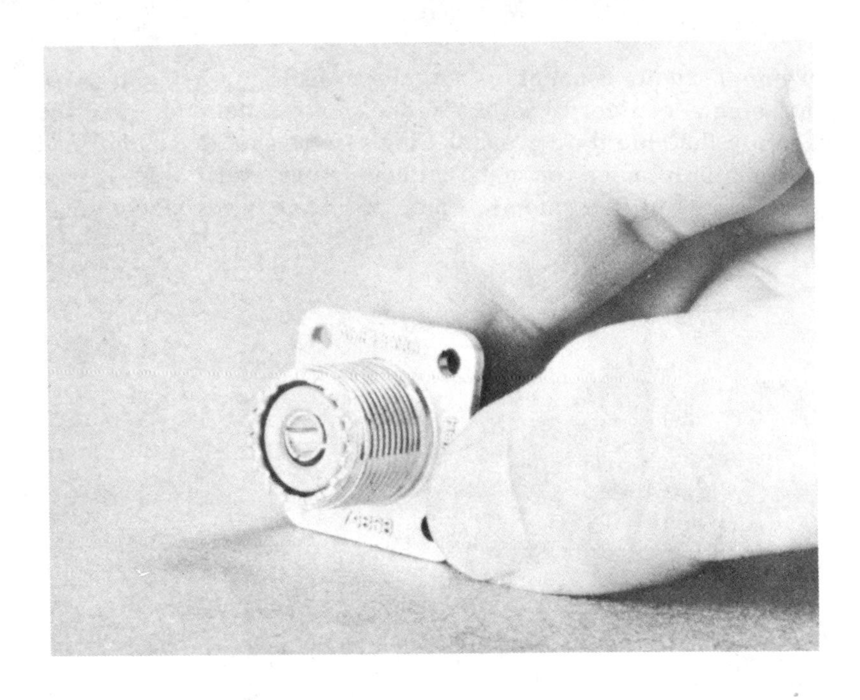

*Fig. 5-11. Closeup 83-1R chassis type RF receptacle. It is normally used with RG-58A/U or RG-8A/U coaxial cable. Courtesy Amphenol RF Div., The Bunker-Ramo Corp.*

microphone with an on-off switch may use a three- or four-wire audio lead. Multiple microphone installations and more complex systems used in broadcast studios may require up to six leads in one cable.

## SPECIAL CONNECTORS

Besides multiple-contact and audio-type connectors, there are hundreds of types designed for special applications—connectors to transfer RF power in VHF-UHF television and two-way communications for example. Again, the cable used with these connectors is normally a shielded type called "coaxial cable," cable specially made for various applications depending on the equipment power, frequency, impedance, and length of cable needed. Schematically, coaxial cable looks like any other shielded lead. A sampling of typical RF connectors is shown in Figs. 5-11 and 5-12.

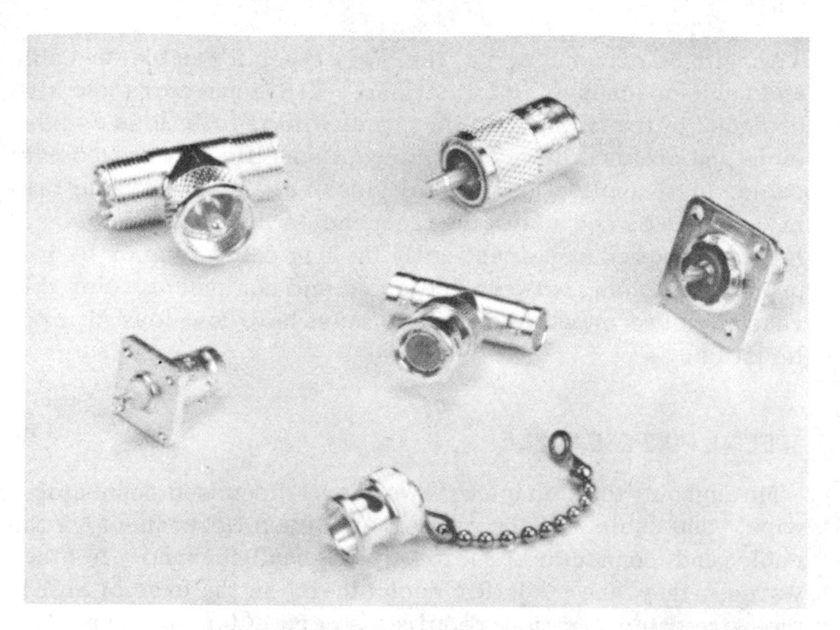

*Fig. 5-12. BNC and UHF RF connectors with tarnish-free, corrosion-resistant surface plating. Courtesy Amphenol Distributor Div., The Bunker-Ramo Corp.*

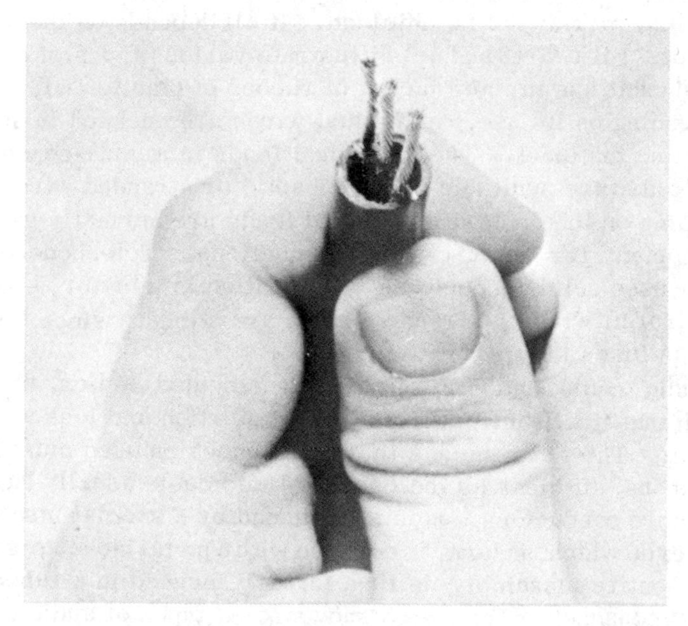

*Fig. 5-13. Control line multi-conductor cable.*

As with other connectors, there are types for cable-to-cable and cable-to-chassis applications. RF connectors are also designed to transfer as much signal with as little loss as possible and are usually made to accept specific sizes of coaxial cable. In RF applications signal losses are more critical than in audio uses because of the frequencies involved. RF signal levels can be reduced drastically by long cable runs or by improper matching between the cable and equipment. For this reason, both connectors and cable must have low-loss characteristics.

## SPECIAL PURPOSE CABLE

Throughout this chapter, we have discussed connectors, wire, and cable. In the case of audio and RF connectors the cable and connector practically go hand-in-hand. In other words, they are made for each other. In the case of multiple-wire cable, it too requires a certain type of connector, but normally this restriction means only that the connector must have enough pins of the correct size to take the wire.

Multiple-wire cable can have any number of individual leads and may or may not be shielded. It all depends on the application. Figs. 5-13 and 5-14 illustrate various types of cable. Most cable has an outer jacket of rubber of plastic and, again depending on its use, individual wires are encased in an insulating material. The iduividual leads in a muli-conductor cable also are available in either solid or stranded wire, depending on the application. Solid leads are normally used in equipment for inter-circuit connections. Telephone cable also uses solid conductors. If vibration is a factor, such as in aircraft wiring, stranded leads are a must, since breakage is less likely.

Audio cable and RF cables, as indicated earlier, must be such that it will introduce as little distortion and loss as possible. This also means that the connectors used must be at least as efficient as the cable. Audio cable usually has one or more conductors, each surrounded by a special insulating material which, in turn, is covered with a metal jacket or shield. The entire assembly is then further encased in a rubber or plastic jacket. Fig. 5-15 shows some types of audio cable. The wire in audio cable is almost always stranded.

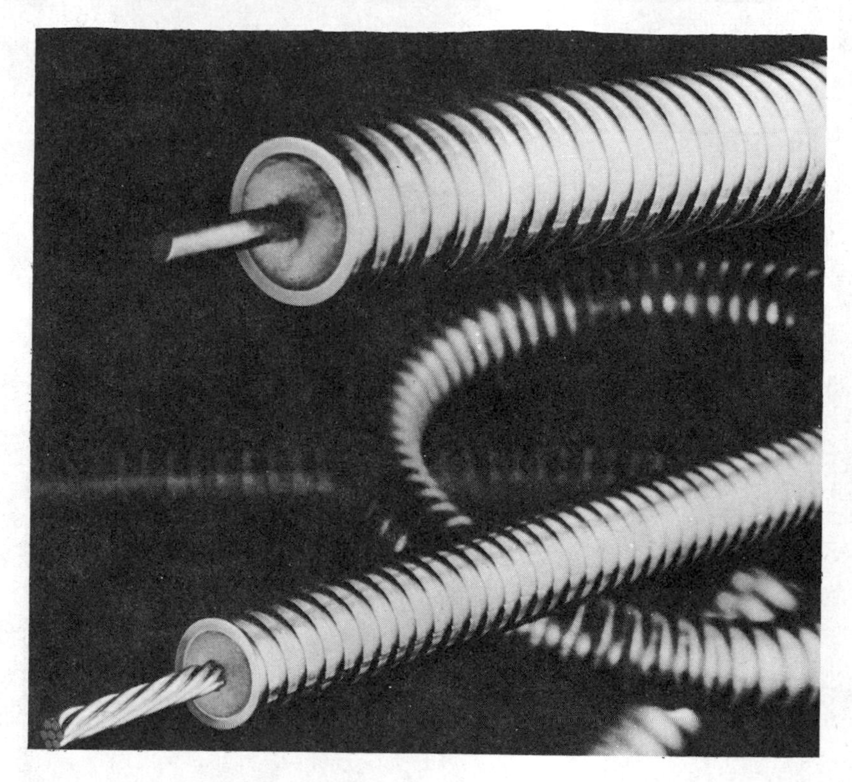

*Fig. 5-14. Coroflex coaxial cable.*

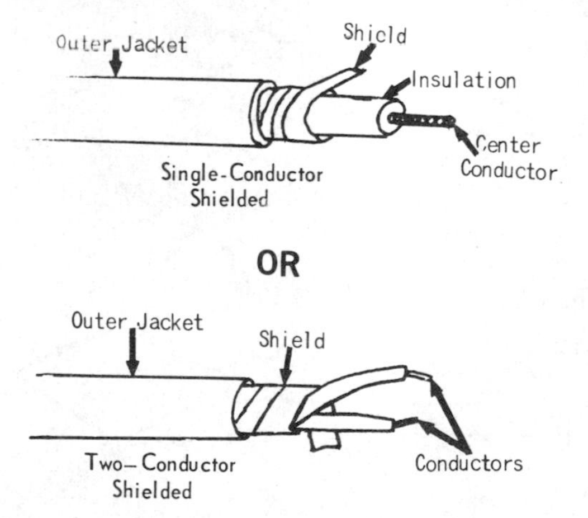


*Fig. 5-15. Sketches illustrating several common types of audio cable.*

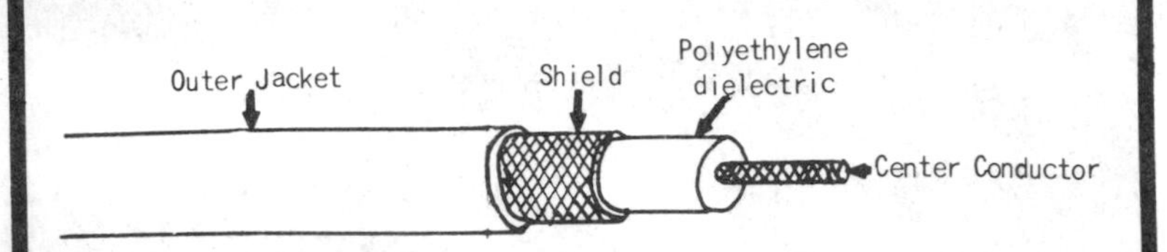


*Fig. 5-16. Drawing showing construction of coaxial cable.*

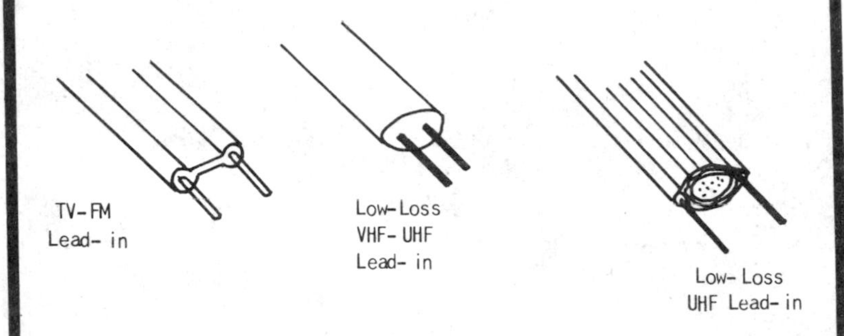


*Fig. 5-17. As these drawings show, TV lead or twin-lead is available in several basic forms.*

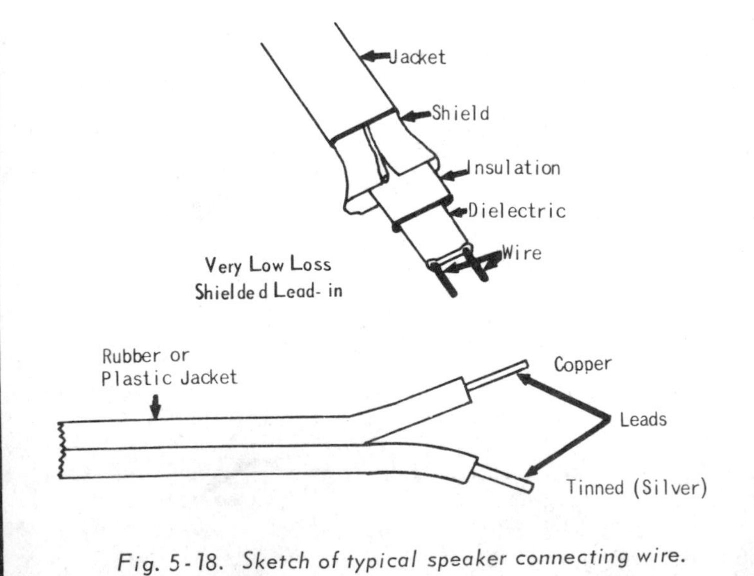


*Fig. 5-18. Sketch of typical speaker connecting wire.*

RF or coaxial cable is also available with either solid or stranded leads. Like audio cable, coax consists of a specially insulated center conductor which is then covered with a metal shield and, finally, by a rubber or plastic jacket. However, unlike audio cable, RF cable has only one center conductor and a shield as shown in Fig. 5-16. The choice of using either solid or stranded coaxial cable depends on the application.

Another type of special cable is "flat lead" or twin-lead as it is commonly called—the two-conductor wire used for TV lead-in. It is simply two wires covered with an insulating material which also separates the leads by a specific measure. Twin-lead comes in several types; some are covered by a foil which acts as shielding. See Fig. 5-17.

Speaker wire is also a two-conductor cable something like appliance cord, only it is not made to handle the current required by an appliance. Typical speaker cable is sketched in Fig. 5-18. Usually, each conductor is stranded and insulated with a rubber or plastic jacket. Speaker wire leads are also color-coded in some way (usually one copper and the other a silver color) to insure proper phasing between speakers.

There are single-conductor cables made for test instrument leads. In most cases, a test cable is a single lead covered with a very heavy insulating jacket. Some also have a shield. The heavy insulation is required for high-voltage protection.

CHAPTER 6

# Types of Diagrams

Before you pack your family into the old bus for a long trip, one of the first things you do is get out the road maps to find the best route to your destination. From experience we know that road maps use codes or symbols to point out camp sites, parks, mileage check points, etc. They may look complicated to a beginner, but after using them a couple of times road maps are really very simple, thanks to a system of symbols. With today's complex highway system, the only way to get across unfamiliar country without getting lost is to use a map.

A home builder uses a road map, too. But a builder's "map" tells him where to place the frame on the foundation and where to locate supports. This type of map is called a "blueprint." An electronic or electrical diagram does the same job for a technician who has to find his way through the complicated maze of wires and parts in a television or radio chassis. Without this valuable diagram, a technician would spend hours just tracing wires from point to point.

## SCHEMATIC DIAGRAMS

Several types of diagrams are used in electronics, but the "schematic" diagram is the most widely known since it is the one used by technicians for service work.

A complete schematic diagram of a transistorized, portable broadcast receiver is shown in Fig. 6-1. At first glance, the uninitiated may see nothing but a jumbled mass of lines with a lot of meaningless numbers and letters. That California road map looked like someone's nightmare, too, at first! But it really isn't a nightmare. Usually, the schematic diagram is drawn so the technician follows the signal path from left to

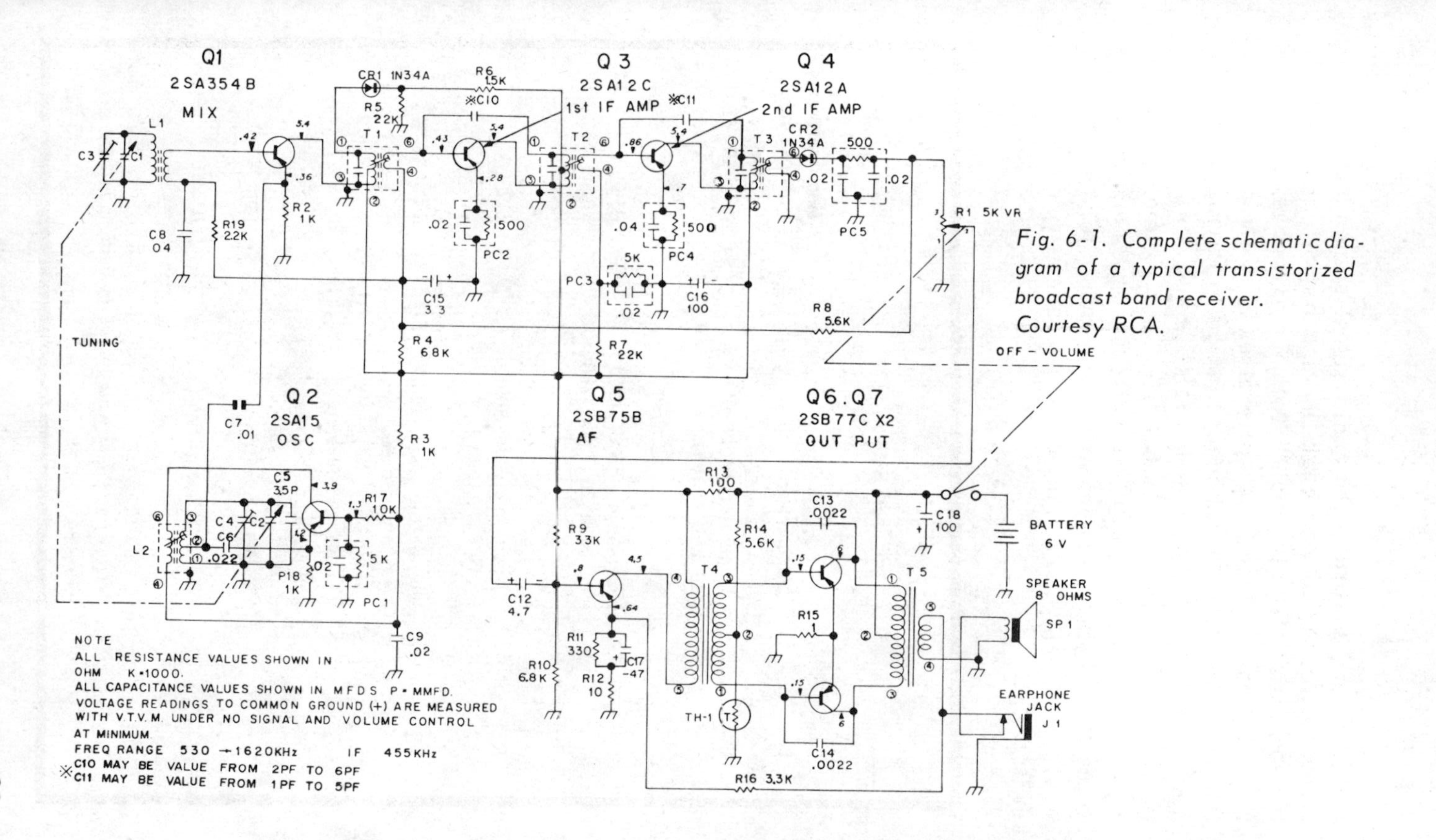


*Fig. 6-1. Complete schematic diagram of a typical transistorized broadcast band receiver. Courtesy RCA.*

right. In other words, the radio signal comes in at L1 (the antenna coil) and goes through the circuits until it comes out the speaker (SP1) at the right. To make parts easier to identify, the manufacturer normally gives each one a number— this is called "component identification." Parts, too, are numbered in order from left to right. Each similar part has the same letter ahead of the number. For example: capacitors are always designated by a C, resistors by an R, and transistors by a Q. There are also symbols for transformers, coils, speakers, and even mechanical parts such as switches.

PARTS LIST

| Symbol No. | Description | Manufacturer's Part Number |
|---|---|---|
| C1 | Capacitor, electrolytic 10 mfd, 100v DC | SRE 159V10 |
| C2 | Capacitor, disc, fixed ceramic, .047 pfd, 100v DC | BPD-05 |
| R1 | Resistor, fixed, 500K ½-watt carbon | E 2517 |
| R2 | Resistor, fixed, 100K ½-watt carbon | BTS-100K |
| T1 | Audio transformer 8400 ohms/3-4 ohms | A-2927 |
| V1 | Tube, converter | IR5 |
| V2 | Tube, IF amplifier | IU4 |

*Fig. 6-2. Partial parts list which usually accompanies a schematic diagram.*

The reason for using symbols to identify capacitors, resistors, etc., is to make the schematic easier to read—the same reason you have symbols on a road map. It would get pretty cluttered up if they didn't. To eliminate this unnecessary mess, the manufacturer provides a separate replacement parts list in the service manual which gives a full description of each component. A portion of a typical parts list is shown in Fig. 6-2.

A service manual is not something you normally get when you buy a radio; you have to request it (with the schematic) from the manufacturer. There are companies who compile schematics and servicing information which they make available through local electronic dealers or automatically on a subscription basis.

In addition to blue-printing the signal path through a piece of electronic or electrical equipment, a schematic also tells the technician what the correct voltage and resistance values should be at specific points in the circuit. Armed with this information and suitable test equipment, he can quickly trace a problem in a TV or radio to the defective component.

## BLOCK DIAGRAMS

A block diagram of a typical broadcast receiver is shown in Fig. 6-3. A block diagram is nothing more than a simplified layout of the electronic circuit using squares or rectangles to illustrate the various stages and to show the path of the signal.

Block diagrams are useful for a quick and easy understanding of the relationship between circuits without the confusion of tracing wires. The various blocks are often labeled to show the tubes or transistors that function in that particular stage and are very helpful in locating stages which perform several functions in more complex circuits. A block diagram is also very helpful in explaining circuit theory and it is widely used for this purpose in many basic electronics courses.

As shown in Fig. 6-3, we can trace an incoming signal from the antenna, through the RF stage, to the mixer stage. Here the signal is "mixed" with a signal from the local oscillator to produce an IF signal, which goes through the IF stages, detector, audio amplifier and finally, to the speaker. Of

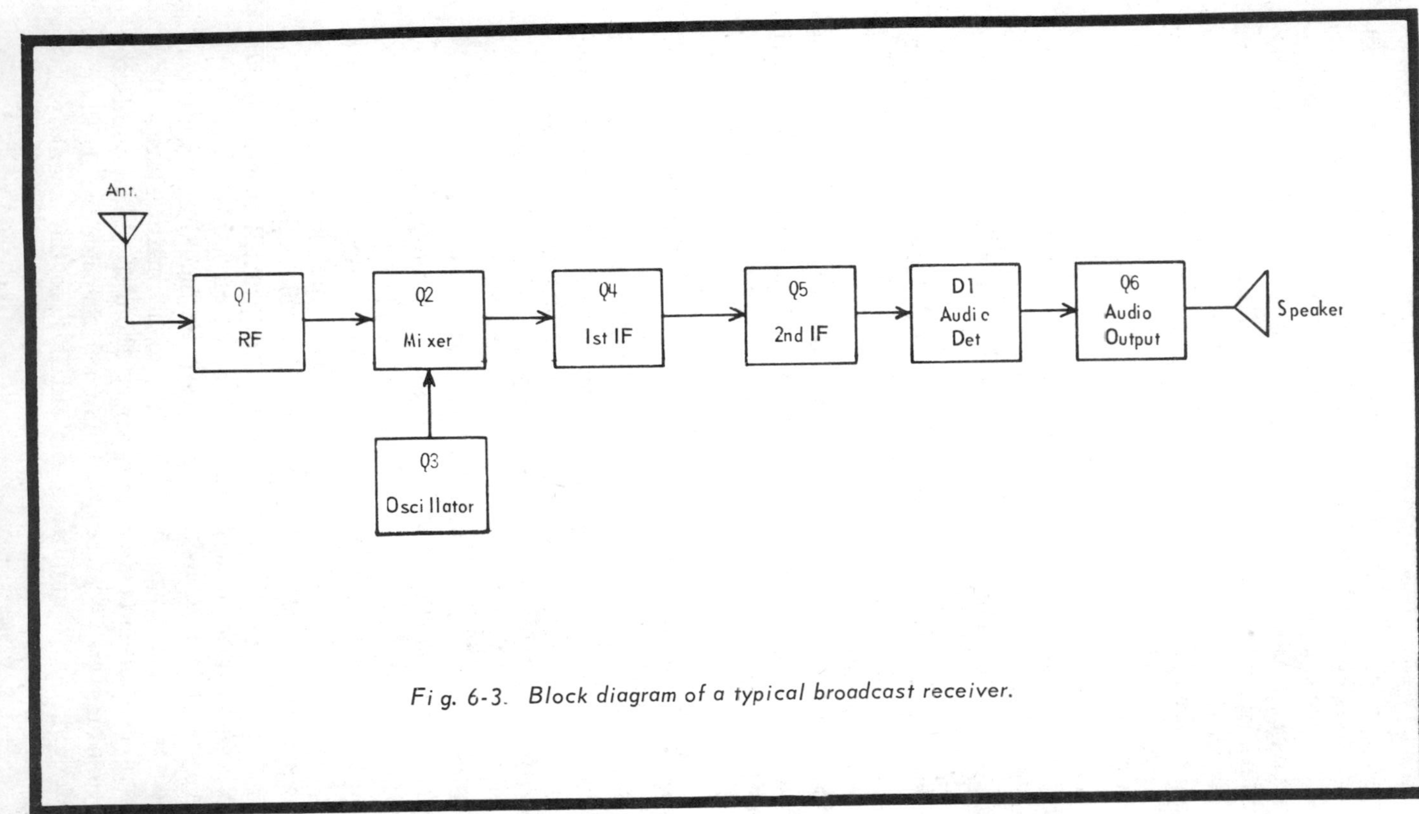


*Fig. 6-3. Block diagram of a typical broadcast receiver.*

course, this is a very brief explanation of how the received signal moves through the radio from the antenna to the speaker, but that is the purpose of a block diagram.

## LAYOUT DIAGRAMS

A layout diagram is nothing more than the physical location of the circuit components. As shown in Fig. 6-4, the diagram indicates the position of tubes, transformers, controls, and even adjustments. This type of diagram is very helpful to a service technician for locating various test points and adjustments during alignment and tube replacement. It is sometimes called a tube placement diagram. Controls or other components shown in dashed lines are located beneath the chassis or below the view being illustrated. The tube diagrams may also have a line or space to show pin orientation to make it easier to re-insert a tube into a socket you can't see.

Although a layout diagram generally illustrates only the major components in tube equipment, layout diagrams of transistorized equipment may be actual photos or drawings of complete circuit boards. Fig. 6-5 shows a transistor circuit board.

## PICTORIAL DIAGRAMS

A typical pictorial diagram or drawing is shown in Fig. 6-6. Similar diagrams are usually used to aid in building of kit-type electronic equipment. The pictorial diagram is suited for this function because it gives the builder a physical view of the actual wiring which is easier for a novice to follow than a complicated wiring diagram. In a rather simple piece of equipment, the pictorial diagram will show all of the components. In more complicated equipment, the components will be installed in groups with a pictorial for each group showing only those particular components. This eliminates confusion for both the builder and the manufacturer.

Newer transistorized equipment use printed-circuit boards which makes kit assembly an easy task for almost anyone. The pictorials for these circuits are usually actual circuit board photos or drawings which show all of the components for that circuit, similar to the diagram in Fig. 6-5.

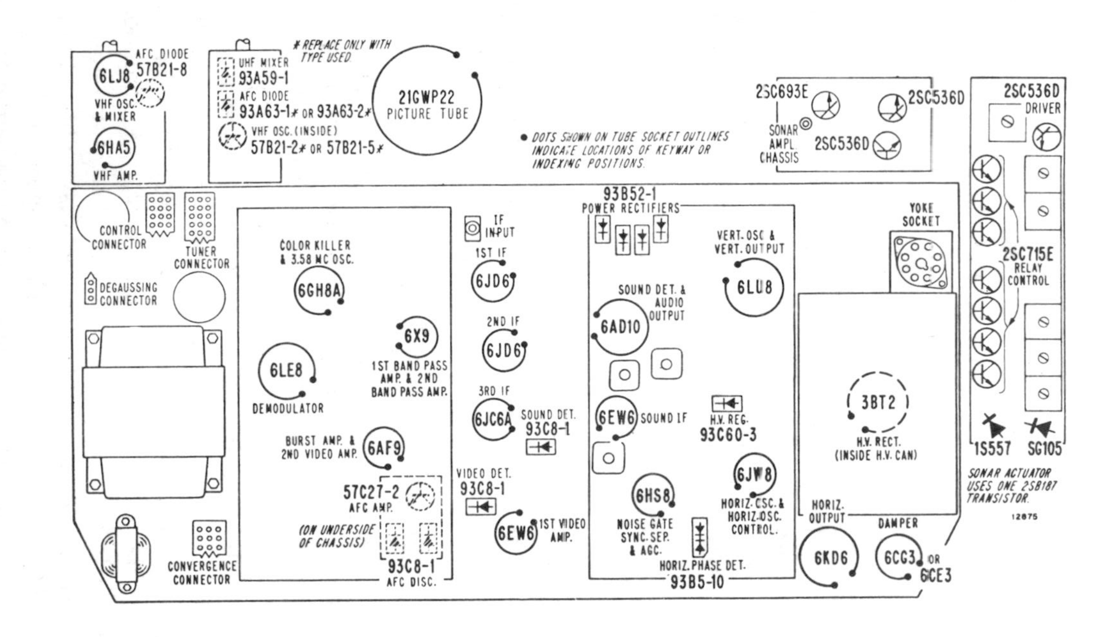


Fig. 6-4. Typical component layout diagram.

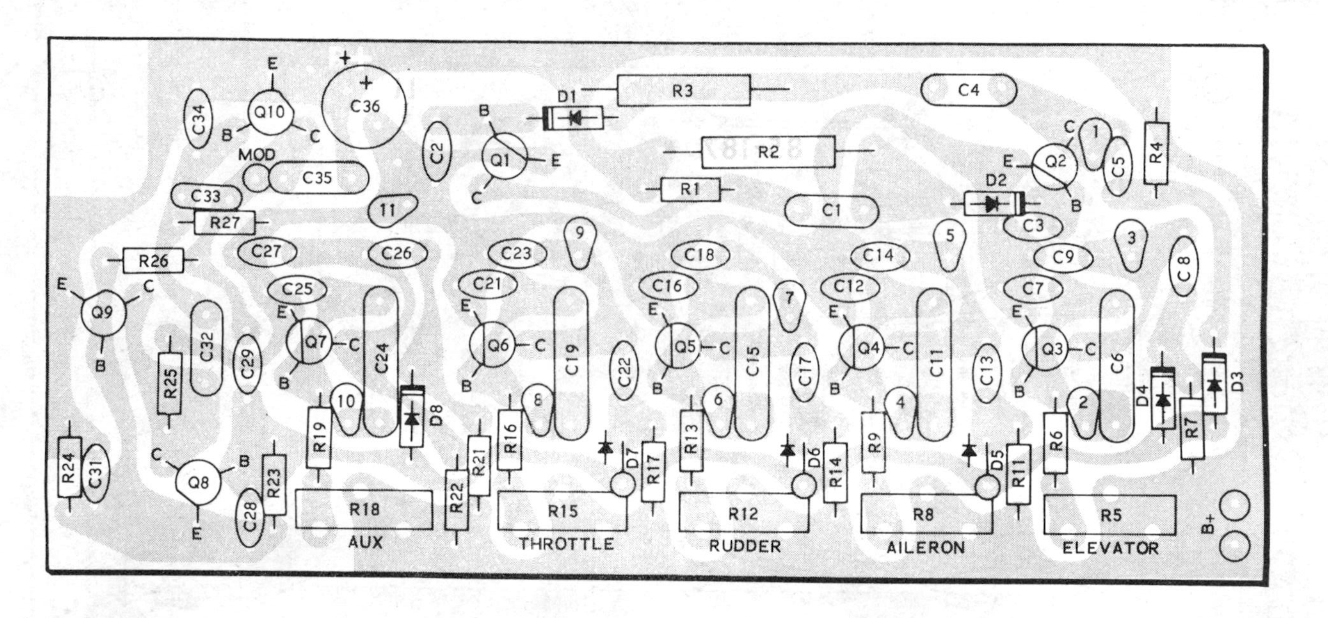

Fig. 6-5. Layout diagram of a typical transistorized circuit board.

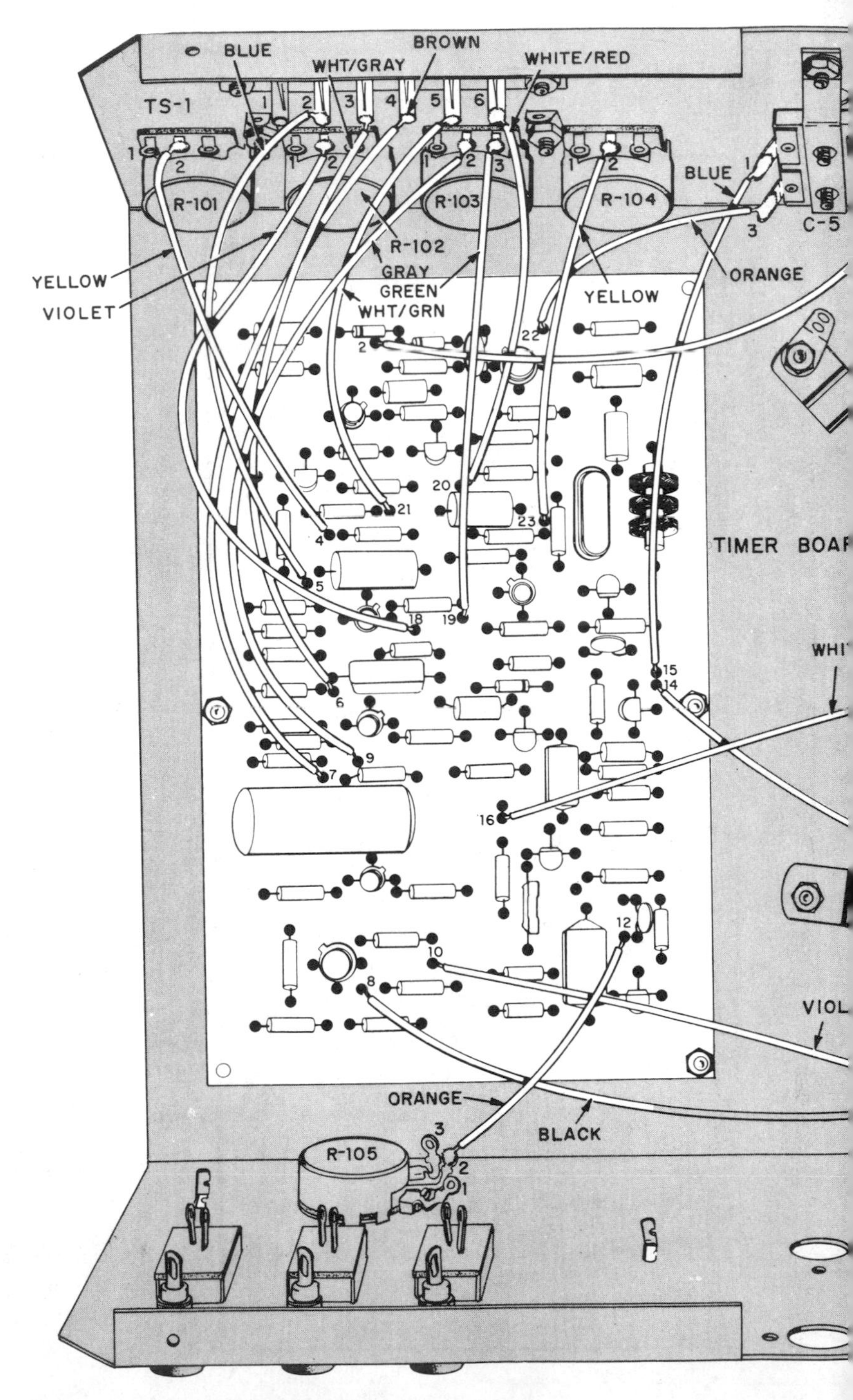


*Fig. 6-6. Typical pictorial diagram showing printed-circuit and component wiring.*

## MECHANICAL CONSTRUCTION DIAGRAMS

This type of diagram is used to show the construction of mechanical components and systems which normally cannot be shown on a schematic or other diagram. Mechanical construction diagrams are used to illustrate such things as tape recorder drive systems, antenna rotators, hydraulic systems, etc. An example of a mechanical construction diagram is the

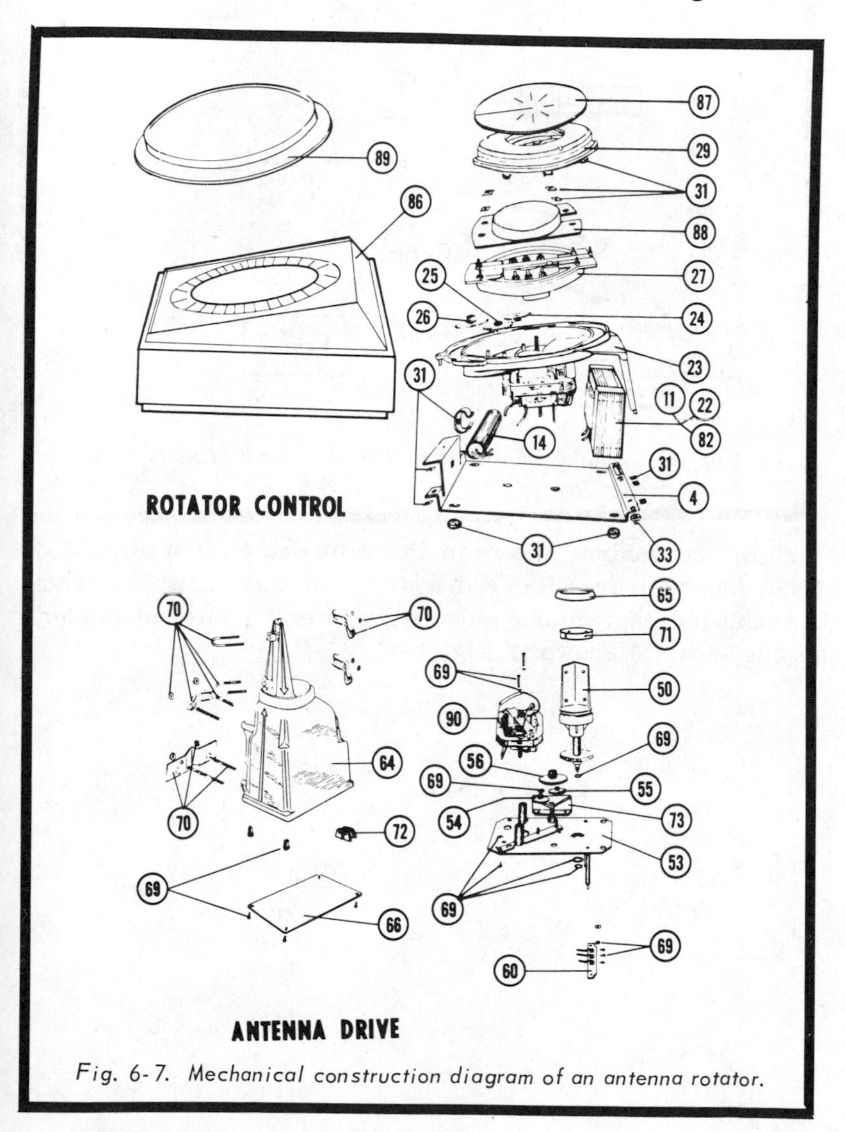


Fig. 6-7. Mechanical construction diagram of an antenna rotator.

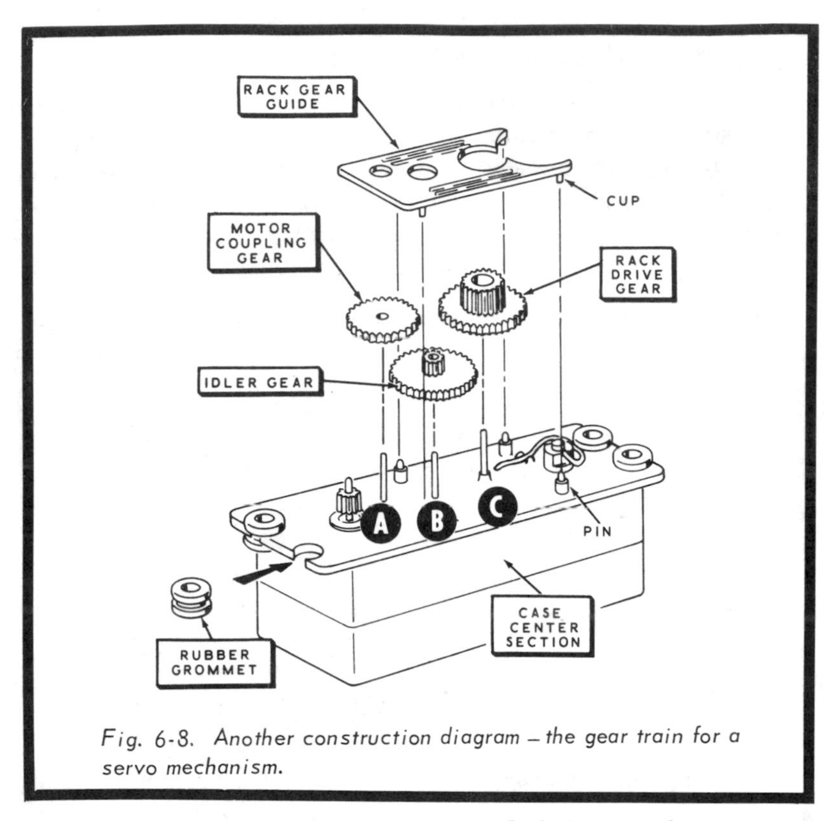

*Fig. 6-8. Another construction diagram – the gear train for a servo mechanism.*

rotator mechanism shown in the exploded view of Fig. 6-7. Such diagrams are often a drawing, cutaway view, or photo. An exploded diagram showing the gear arrangement of an electronic servo is shown in Fig. 6-8.

CHAPTER 7

# Radio & TV Schematics

Most portable AM radios today are transistorized and follow approximately the same basic design established by tube-type receivers. To begin with, let's consider a relatively common AM circuit and work into the larger, more complex electronic equipment as we go along. Even though the schematic in Fig. 7-1 represents a transistorized receiver the same explanation is basically valid for a tube unit. Fig. 7-2 shows a block diagram of the same receiver.

From the preceding Chapters, we should recognize most of the components in the receiver, so let's go through the schematic to see what it tells us.

A schematic diagram, as you recall, usually begins with the input (received) signal entering at the left, going through the circuits to the right. So let's imagine we turn the receiver on. The loop antenna (L1) is constantly "intercepting" radio signals. In order to receive a particular AM broadcast station, the loop antenna and tuning capacitors CA-1 and CA-2 must be set to accept that signal. So we turn the dial, which also moves CA-1 and CA-2. When a station is tuned in, the signal passes through the L1/CA-1 circuit and associated components to the first receiver stage, Q1. This stage is labeled CONV, the abbreviation for converter.

The converter is a combination RF amplifier, oscillator, and mixer in most receivers of this type. It amplifies the received broadcast signal and mixes it with an internally-generated signal (oscillator signal). The output from the converter as a result of this "mixing" is another signal called the "IF" or intermediate frequency signal. It contains the program material broadcast from the station. The RF signal originally picked up by the antenna is simply used as a means of "carrying" the audio signals through space. Once it

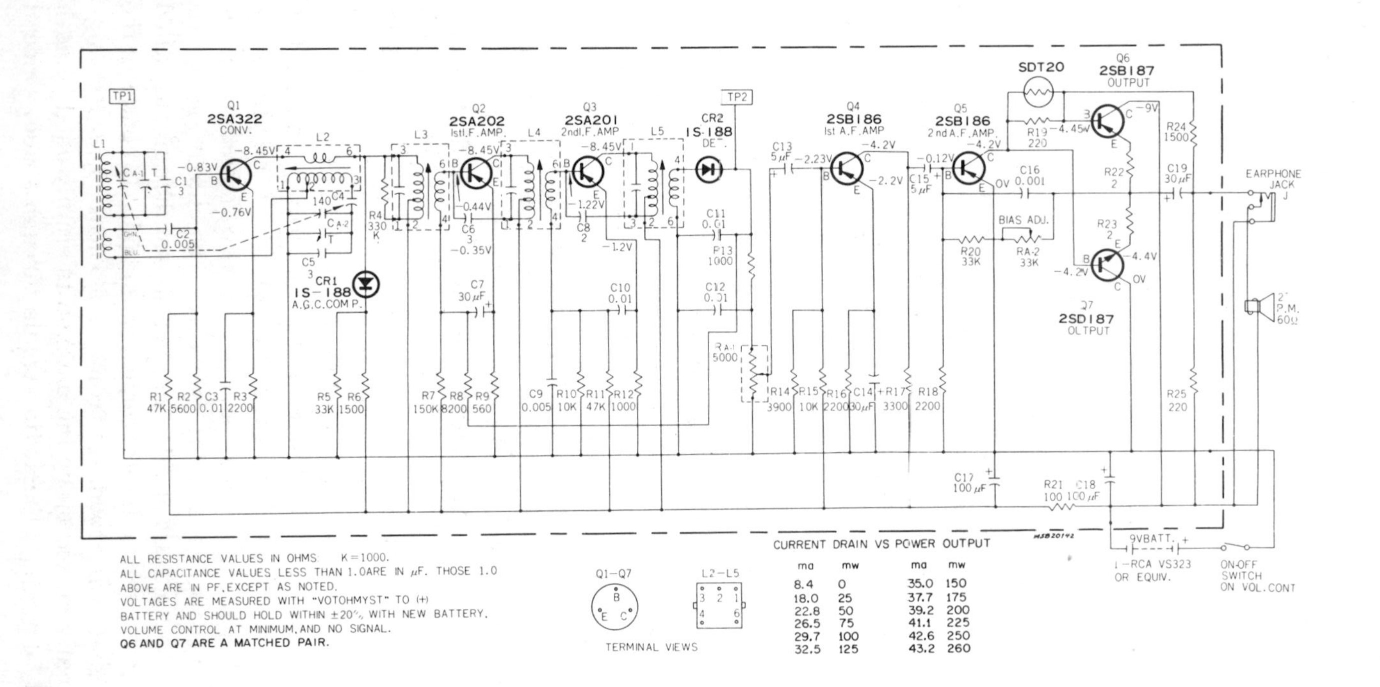


ALL RESISTANCE VALUES IN OHMS. K=1000.
ALL CAPACITANCE VALUES LESS THAN 1.0ARE IN μF. THOSE 1.0 ABOVE ARE IN PF.EXCEPT AS NOTED.
VOLTAGES ARE MEASURED WITH "VOTOHMYST" TO (+) BATTERY AND SHOULD HOLD WITHIN ±20%, WITH NEW BATTERY. VOLUME CONTROL AT MINIMUM, AND NO SIGNAL.
**Q6 AND Q7 ARE A MATCHED PAIR.**

CURRENT DRAIN VS POWER OUTPUT

| ma | mw | ma | mw |
|---|---|---|---|
| 8.4 | 0 | 35.0 | 150 |
| 18.0 | 25 | 37.7 | 175 |
| 22.8 | 50 | 39.2 | 200 |
| 26.5 | 75 | 41.1 | 225 |
| 29.7 | 100 | 42.6 | 250 |
| 32.5 | 125 | 43.2 | 260 |

*Fig. 7-1. Schematic of a typical, small transistorized radio.. Courtesy RCA.*

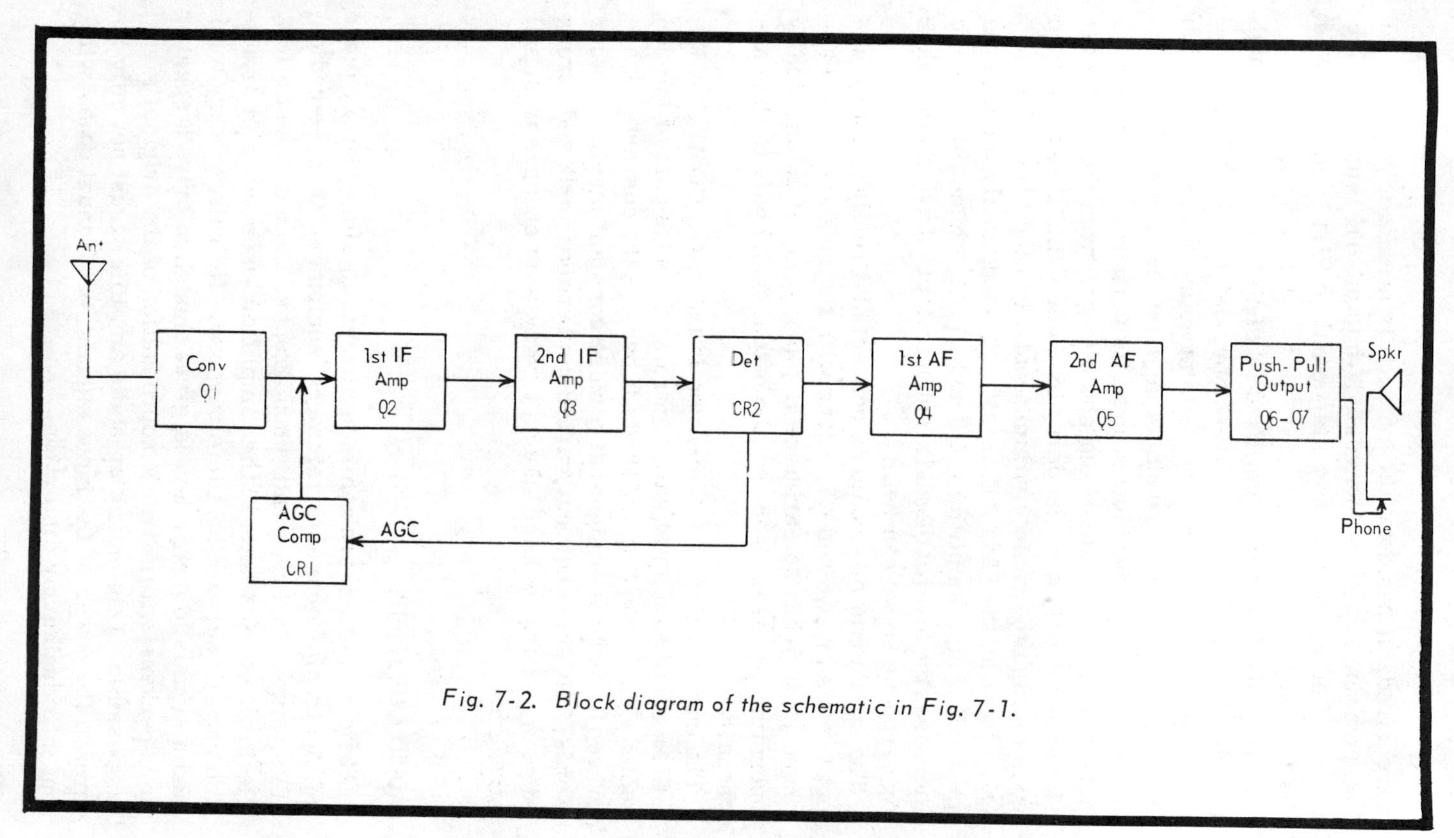


*Fig. 7-2. Block diagram of the schematic in Fig. 7-1.*

is received, it has done its job so it is no longer needed. So the incoming signal is "converted" into an "IF" signal which is amplified by the next two stages called "1st IF amp" and "2nd IF amp."

At the output of Q3 the amplified IF signal is coupled through transformer L5 to a detector—abbreviated "DET" on the schematic. This stage is nothing more than a diode which passes only the audio broadcast signals; the IF signal is eliminated as it too has now served its purpose. So now all we have left is a duplicate of the audio signal from the broadcast studio at the output of the detector diode CR2. The audio then goes through the radio's volume control to the "1st AF amp," Q4, then to the "2nd AF amp," Q5, and finally through the pushpull audio amplifiers Q6 and Q7. Each amplifier stage increases the level of the audio sufficiently to drive the speaker or earphone so we can hear it.

The speaker in this radio is connected directly to audio output transistors Q6 and Q7, along with the closed-circuit earphone jack. When an earphone is plugged in, it automatically opens the speaker lead so the output is fed only to the earphone.

The only stage we didn't mention is the "AGC COMP," CR1. AGC means "automatic gain control." It takes part of the detected signal from CR2 and feeds it back to the converter stage to keep the volume or signal at a more constant level. In other words, it smoothes out variations between weak and strong signals so the volume doesn't vary with changes in signal strength.

## AUDIO AMPLIFIERS

Audio amplifiers are common circuits in almost every piece of electronic home entertainment equipment today—radios, TVs, tape players, and phonographs, to name just a few. Regardless of whether the amplifier uses tubes or transistors, it serves the same purpose. It "raises" very weak audio signals to power levels great enough to drive a speaker (or speakers) with as true a reproduction of the original signal as possible. This means an audio amplifier must not only increase the power of the input signals, but it must do so without introducing any distortion.

Audio amplifiers are classed as being either monaural or stereo. A monaural amplifier is a unit having a single input channel and one audio output channel to a speaker or headphones. A stereo unit has two channels or speaker outputs and naturally, two separate input channels.

### Monaural Amplifier

The schematic diagram of a popular audio amplifier is shown in Fig. 7-3 (foldout Panel A). The block diagram in Fig. 7-4 (foldout Panel A) better illustrates the various stages and their relationship to each other.

As shown in Fig. 7-4, the amplifier has three basic sections—the magnetic phono preamplifier, a main amplifier, and the power supply. Fig. 7-4 shows a block labeled "source selector." This is actually the selector switch shown on the schematic. It is used to switch any one of four inputs to the main amplifier. The magnetic phono input uses a preamplifier, one half of a 6EU7 tube, to boost the signal before it reaches the main amplifier. A preamplifier is necessary because a magnetic phono pickup provides a relatively low output voltage and so requires additional preamplification.

Referring to the schematic and block diagram, the input signals are fed through the selector switch to a high-gain amplifier, V1B, the other half of the preamplifier tube. The amplified signal from the plate of V1B then goes through a coupling capacitor to the volume control, a variable resistor which determines the amount of signal fed to the next stage, V2A. From V2A the signal goes through an RC (resistor/capacitor) tone control network. The dotted lines around this network indicate that it is a "packaged" or encapsulated unit. The bass and treble controls in the tone circuit are mounted on the amplifier front panel.

From the tone control network, the amplified signal is fed through a length of shielded audio cable to the grid of another amplifier, V2B. Then, it is further amplified by V3A and fed to V3B. V3B is not an amplifier but a "phase splitter." Its purpose is to apply the signal in the proper phase through coupling capacitor C16 to the grid of V4 and through coupling capacitor C17 to the grid of V5. V4 and V5 are the pushpull power output stage which feeds the speaker. As shown, the audio power output stage is coupled to the speaker through a multi-impedance transformer. This transformer allows a choice of any three speaker impedances, a feature which is useful for a custom installation, and it provides for a wider choice of speakers.

Voltages for the entire amplifier are furnished by a common power supply. Various voltage taps are used to provide the necessary plate, screen, and filament voltages.

## Stereo Amplifier

Having considered a monaural or single-channel audio amplifier, let's see what a dual-channel or stereo amplifier looks like. Referring to the schematic diagram of Fig. 7-5 (foldout Panel B) and the block diagram in Fig. 7-6 (foldout Panel E), we see that this stereo amplifier has a common DC power supply, a phono preamp circuit, a control preamp circuit, and a power amplifier for each of the two channels.

Stereo channels are normally labeled "left" and "right." Also, since a stereo amplifier has two identical circuits, it is necessary to describe only one of them, so let's look at the left channel. It is also important to point out the numbering designations often used in a stereo amplifier of this type. Looking at the schematic, we notice that the left-channel transistors are designated with the letter "L" while transistors in the right channel are designated "R." For example, Q1L, and Q101L are left-channel transistors.

Referring to the schematic of Fig. 7-5 (foldout Panel B) we notice two phonograph inputs—one for each channel. These inputs come from the stereo pickup cartridge in the phonograph arm. Amplifiers Q1L and Q2L are preamps for the phonograph input. The output of each preamp goes to a "source switch," as do the other input connections. The source switch, as in the monaural amplifier, simply selects the input to the control preamplifier circuit shown within the large dotted box.

From the selector or source switch, the input signal goes through Q101L, an "emitter-follower," which is used to provide an output to a tape recorder if desired. The emitter-follower circuit provides an impedance match between the high input impedance and the low output impedance for the tape recorder. A switch called "tape monitor" routes the signal from Q101L either to the tape recorder, if used, or to the next transistor stage, Q102L, if the tape recorder is not used.

In the "off" position as shown, the signal from Q101L is fed through C103 and R117 to the base of Q102L. Q102L is another emitter-follower which provides a low-impedance driving source to the tone controls.

If the tape monitor switch is in the "on" position, the signal from Q101L is applied to the tape recorder where it can be recorded and immediately played back because the tape recorder monitor (tape mon) signal is fed back through R101, C103, R117, Q102L, and on to the tone controls.

The output of Q102L is applied to the base and treble tone controls at the same time and the signal from these circuits is coupled to the base of Q103L. The treble tone control consists of R147, R149, and C119, while the base tone control circuit consists of R139, R141, R143, R145, C115, and C117.

Q103L amplifies and inverts the signal. Inverting the signal means that the signal from the output or collector of Q103L will be of the opposite "phase" from its input (base) signal. This type of circuit design is used to provide better base response. The output of Q103L is also coupled through C123 and the "tone flat" switch in the "off" position to the balance control. When the tone flat switch is in the "on" position, the tone controls and Q103L are not used. The output of Q102L goes directly from C113 to the balance control.

The "balance" controls in both left and right channels are mechanically linked in a special control so that at the center of rotation the output of each channel to its volume control is at maximum. Turning the balance control clockwise reduces the left channel output to its volume control but does not affect the right channel. Counterclockwise rotation of the control reduces the right-channel output and does not affect the left channel.

The volume control in this unit is a dual type connected so that it will "raise" or "lower" the left and right channels together. When the loudness control is in the "on" position, the volume control acts like a loudness control. This type of control allows the operator to compensate for his own aural response to audio frequency signals at lower listening levels.

C125, C127, and R161 make up the loudness circuit when the loudness control is in the "on" position.

From the volume control, signals are coupled through C129 to the base of Q104L. They are amplified in Q104L and direct-coupled to the base of another emitter-follower, Q105L. From the emitter of Q105L, the signal is fed to the power amplifier circuit (left channel).

The signal from Q105L is coupled through C201 and R201 to the base of Q201L. Q201L and Q202L amplify the signals and apply them through C207 and R215 to a predriver transistor, Q203L, where they are further amplified. The signals from the collector of Q203L are then coupled directly to the base of Q205L and through diodes D201L, D202L, and D203L to the base of Q204L. The reason for these diodes is to provide the proper bias voltage for "Class AB" operation of the driver and power output stage. The output of Q204L and Q205L are fed to the bases of Q206L and Q207L. The output of the power transistors is fed directly to the speaker.

The power output circuits in this unit are protected by current-limiting zener diodes, ZD204L and ZD205L, emitter resistors R235 and R237, and capacitor C217. If a short circuit or severe overload occurs, which results in more than five amps of current flow, the reverse-biased zener diodes clamp or restrict the driver transistor voltage to a level which prevents any further increase in output current.

The dotted line labeled "thermal coupled," from Q206L to a thermal circuit breaker, is also a protective device. If the power output current goes higher than normal, and the output transistor reaches 60°C, the thermal circuit breaker mounted on the heat sink with the output transistors opens and interrupts the power supply voltage.

The right channel in this stereo unit operates the same as the left. The power supply, as in the monaural unit, provides various DC voltages to the transistor circuits with one full-wave bridge rectifier (D306, 307, 308, and 309) and one full-wave rectifier (D303, and D304). Q301 and Q302 function as high-gain amplifiers to provide adequate filtering of the 50v DC supply to the phono preamp stages and as a 27v DC source for the amplifier circuits.

## AM- FM / FM STEREO TUNERS

Now let's get into the more complicated entertainment units which combine an AM receiver, an FM receiver, and FM stereo. A schematic diagram of a popular unit in this category is shown in Fig. 7-7 (foldout Panel D) and a block diagram in Fig. 7-8 (foldout Panel C). However, because of the complexity of the unit, we will break it into sections and explain them one by one.

As shown in the complete schematic diagram in Fig. 7-7, the unit consists of an FM tuning circuit, an AM RF amplifier, an FM-AM circuit, multiplex converter, and a power supply. Notice the receiver does not contain audio output circuits. A separate power amplifier is needed.

### FM Tuning Circuit

As shown in Fig. 7-7, the "local" position of the local-distance switch couples the input FM signal from the line-cord antenna to input transformer T1 in the FM tuning circuit. When the switch is in the "distance" position, the input signal to T1 is derived from an external FM antenna. The secondary of the input transformer is connected into a circuit tuned by C101. This capacitor is a part of the main FM tuning capacitor and is used to select the received signal, which is then coupled through C105 to the emitter of RF amplifier Q1.

The RF amplifier operates as a grounded-base circuit which increases the input signal level and couples it to another tuned circuit made up of L1, C102, and a trimmer capacitor, C107. An AGC signal, such as we mentioned earlier in our discussion of AM receivers, is coupled from the first IF amplifier to the base of RF amplifier Q1 to decrease its gain on stronger input signals.

The input signal selected by the tuned circuit in the collector of Q1 is coupled through C108 to the base of mixer transistor Q2. The coil connected after C108 acts as a 10.7-MHz trap to short out any 10.7-MHz IF signals that may be present there. Q3 is a grounded-base oscillator, and its frequency is determined by a tuned circuit consisting of C103, C114, and L3. C113 is a feedback capacitor for the oscillator. A small DC voltage, applied through R106 to diode D101, is fed from the ratio detector circuit. The voltage changes when the frequency of the oscillator begins to drift; therefore, it is called an "AFC voltage" or automatic frequency control voltage. It actually changes the capacity of the oscillator's tuned circuit, which in turn changes the oscillator frequency.

The output of the oscillator is coupled through C115 to the base of mixer transistor Q2. The frequency of the oscillator is adjusted to produce a signal that is 10.7 MHz higher than the input (received) signal from the RF amplifier. These two signals "mix" or "beat" together, as in an AM receiver, and produce an IF signal output that contains the modulation present in the incoming signal. The IF signal is then coupled through transformer T2 to the FM-IF amplifier circuits.

### FM IF Circuit

From the FM tuning circuit the 10.7-MHz IF signal is coupled through C207 to the base of the first FM-IF amplifier, Q7. Diode D202 and resistors R219, 212, and 211 form a biasing voltage-divider network for the base circuit of Q7. As shown on schematic diagram Fig. 7-7 (foldout Panel D), a small amount of signal voltage from the collector of Q9 is fed back through C215 to the junction of D202 and R219. The signal voltage is rectified by D202 to produce a control voltage proportional to the strength of the incoming signal which in turn changes the bias at the base of Q7.

This action is known as AGC and it allows Q7 to amplify weaker incoming signals more than the stronger ones. Since AGC is directly coupled to the base of Q7, an amplified AGC voltage appears across Q7's emitter resistor, R214. The amplified AGC is then coupled through resistors R213 and R102 to the base of Q1 and to the base of "squelch" amplifier Q12, which we will discuss later. R211, a variable resistor, sets the bias voltage at the base of Q7 to attain the best operating point.

From the collector of Q7 the amplified IF signal is coupled through transformer T3 to the base of the second IF amplifier, Q8. Bias for Q8 is supplied by a voltage divider consisting of R215 and R216. Amplified IF from the collector of Q8 is then coupled through damping resistor R218 to the primary of IF transformer T4. From the secondary of T4 the

FM-IF signal is fed to the base of Q9. Base bias for Q9 is furnished by R221 and R222. From the collector of Q9 the IF signal is coupled through R224 and IF transformer T5 to the base of limiter transistor Q10.

Due to high base bias voltage and a low collector voltage, Q10 clips or limits the amplitude of signal voltages. This "limiting" action eliminates any amplitude modulation (AM) which may be riding on the FM signal. Bias for Q10 is supplied by voltage-divider R225 and R226. Bypass capacitors C208, 211, 212, 213, 214, 216, and 217 keep the emitters and the "cold" ends of the IF transformer secondaries at RF ground potential. Part of the limiter voltage developed across emitter resistor R227 is fed to the tuning meter circuit.

## RATIO DETECTOR

From the output (collector circuit) of Q10, the IF signal is coupled through R228 and ratio detector transformer T10 to the detector circuit. This circuit separates the audio signal from the 10-MHz IF signal. Fig. 7-9 shows this portion of the circuit in greater detail. Transformer T10 is represented by primary coil LA, a center-tapped secondary composed of coils LB and LC, and a third or tertiary winding, LD. LD is just a few turns of wire wrapped tightly around the bottom of primary LA.

Consider a separate voltage as being induced by the primary into each of the secondary windings—LB, LC, and LD. Since

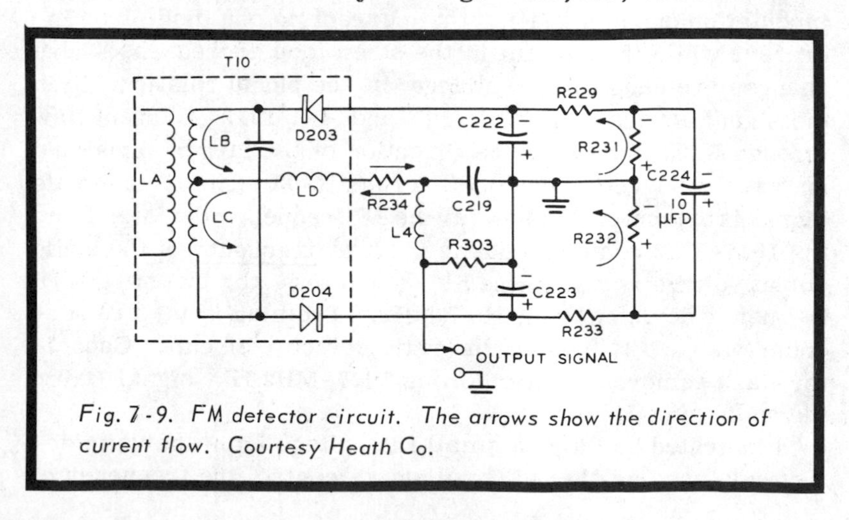


*Fig. 7-9. FM detector circuit. The arrows show the direction of current flow. Courtesy Heath Co.*

LD is closely coupled to the primary, it introduces a voltage that is in series with both LB and LC. The voltage across LD is relatively constant in amplitude as long as the voltage across LA does not change, and the voltage across LD is held constant by the clamping action of Q10.

Each diode has its own separate loop through which current flows as indicated by the arrows. The current in D203 is controlled by the voltage induced in LB and LC which charges C222. The current in D204 is controlled by the voltage induced in LC and LD which charges C223. Since coil LD is common to both current loops, current flows through it in both directions. Electrolytic capacitor C224 is connected across C222 and C223 through R229 and R233 to keep the total voltage across these two capacitors from changing. Thus, any amplitude modulation on the FM signal will be damped out by C224.

Audio output signal from the ratio detector circuit is taken from choke coil L4, across R303 to ground. Notice that the two loop currents are flowing in opposite directions through R234, R303, and L4. At the FM-IF center frequency of 10.7 MHz, the diode currents are equal, so they tend to cancel each other and no voltage appears across R303. Choke L4 helps to prevent any IF from reaching the multiplex circuit. As shown in Fig. 7-7 (foldout Panel D), R303 is actually located on the multiplex circuit board and choke L4 is mounted on the chassis.

When the IF frequency deviates from 10.7 MHz, due to FM modulation (audio signal), the current in one diode loop increases while the current in the other loop decreases. These changes are caused by a change in the phase relationship in the signal across coils LB/LD and LC/LD. Current flow through R303 is now in the direction of the larger signal and an output voltage is developed across R303. The level of this signal is determined by how far the IF frequency deviates from the 10.7-MHz center frequency. The <u>frequency</u> of the audio output voltage is determined by how often the incoming IF frequency deviates from 10.7 MHz. The slug in the T10 secondary is used to balance the ratio detector circuit. Capacitor C219 removes any remaining 10.7-MHz IF signal from the audio signal.

Ad indicated earlier, a small DC voltage from the ratio detector is used as the AFC voltage to control the frequency of oscillator Q3. When properly tuned to an FM station, the DC voltage from the ratio detector is zero. As the oscillator is detuned (oscillator drift), in either direction, the DC voltage will vary in proportion—plus or minus—with respect to ground, depending on which way the tuning changed.

A small signal is also taken from the emitter of limiter transistor Q10 and applied to the negative terminal of the tuning meter. When the mode switch is in the FM or stereo position, R5, R6, R7 and R10 form a voltage-divider network to allow the meter to be "zeroed" when no signal is being received.

### AM Circuit RF Stage

The incoming AM signal is coupled to the base of FM amplifier Q4 from the secondary winding of the rod antenna. The primary of the antenna is connected in a tuned circuit with C1, a portion of the AM tuning capacitor, and trimmer capacitor C4. External antenna signals are fed directly to the base of Q4 through C5. The power to activate the AM RF amplifier circuit comes through terminals 12 and 13 of the mode switch when it is placed in the AM position. The output signal from the collector of Q4 is coupled through a tuned circuit consisting of the primary of T6, C2 (part of the tuning capacitor), and trimmer C9. The input signal (station) selected by this tuned circuit is amplified by Q4 and coupled through T6 to Q5 on the FM-AM circuit board.

### AM Mixer-Oscillator

The remainder of the AM circuit is composed of a conventional oscillator-mixer. IF amplifier, and AM detector. The RF signal from the collector of Q4 is coupled through C201 to the base of Q5, which is the oscillator-mixer circuit. The oscillator circuit is formed by coil T7, tuning capacitor C3, and trimmer capacitor C10. Q5's emitter is connected to ground through C203 and part of oscillator coil T7. A portion of this same winding is connected in a tuned circuit with C3. A separate winding is connected from IF transformer T8 to ground to provide a feedback path to the Q5 collector circuit.

## AM IF Circuit

The input signal from the RF stage and the oscillator signal are combined or "mixed" in Q5 to produce an IF signal at a frequency of 455 kHz. This signal is then coupled through IF transformer T8 to the base of IF amplifier Q6.

As in the case of FM operation, a small signal from the secondary of T9 is made available to the tuning meter through the mode switch when in the AM position.

## AM Detector

The 455-kHz IF signal from the collector of Q6 is coupled through IF transformer T9 and "detected" by diode D201. C205 serves a filtering purpose. The detected audio signal is then fed to the output emitter-followers, C21 and Q22, to lugs 2 and 14 of the mode switch.

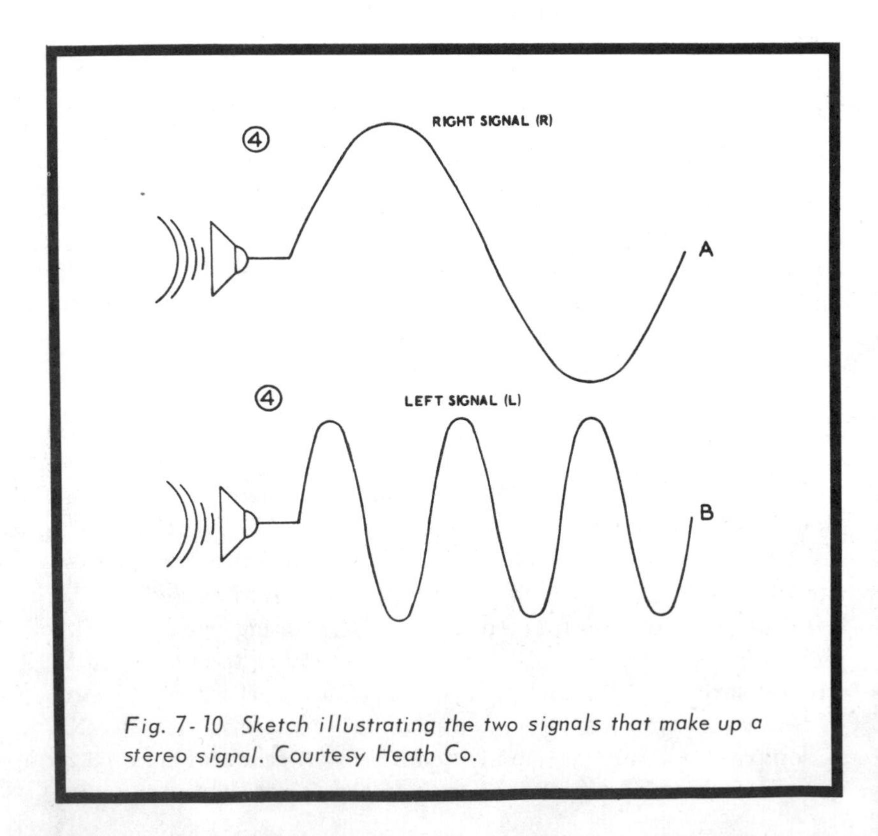


*Fig. 7-10 Sketch illustrating the two signals that make up a stereo signal. Courtesy Heath Co.*

## Multiplex Circuit

The waveforms in Fig. 7-10A and B show samples of signals that might appear at the left (L) and right (R) channels of a stereo signal broadcast by a radio station. The transmitting circuits at the station combine these signals to produce an L plus R signal and the L minus R signal shown in Fig. 7-11. These two signals are then combined with the 19-kHz pilot signal (Fig. 7-11C) and the whole thing is sent out from the broadcasting station as a multiplex signal.

The diagram in Fig. 7-12 shows approximately where these signals are in a stereo FM signal spectrum. The L plus R signal carries the audio information (from 50 Hz to 15 kHz) and is referred to as the "main channel." Monaural FM tuners use only this part of the signal—the remaining stereo signals are taken out by networks in the tuner.

The L minus R signal, which is amplitude-modulated (AM), is transmitted on a 38-kHz subcarrier, often called the subcarrier channel. A second subcarrier signal is also sometimes transmitted at a frequency of 67 kHz. This channel, used to transmit commercial music, is referred to as the SCA (Subsidiary Communications Authorization) channel.

The signal from the ratio detector that appears across R303 is coupled through C301 to the base of Q13. Between stations, Q13 is cut off by a voltage from squelch amplifier Q12. We indicated earlier that an AGC voltage was fed to the base of Q12 from the emitter of Q7 when a station was tuned in. Squelch control R301, which is connected in a voltage-divider network with R302 in the emitter of Q12, is adjusted so that Q12 is cut off. When the receiver is tuned between FM stations, the AGC voltage becomes less positive and Q12 begins to conduct. When Q12 conducts, its collector current flows through R307 at the emitter of Q13. The added current increases the voltage drop across R307 which cuts off Q13 so that noise between stations does not pass into the circuit.

The diagram and waveforms shown in Fig. 7-13 (foldout Panel F), in conjunction with the schematic in Fig. 7-7 (foldout Panel D), should give you a clearer understanding of how the multiplex section of this receiver operates. Starting at amplifier Q13, the FM signal is coupled through C302 to the base of Q14. This transistor stage does two things: A 19-kHz tuned circuit in the collector, consisting of T12 and

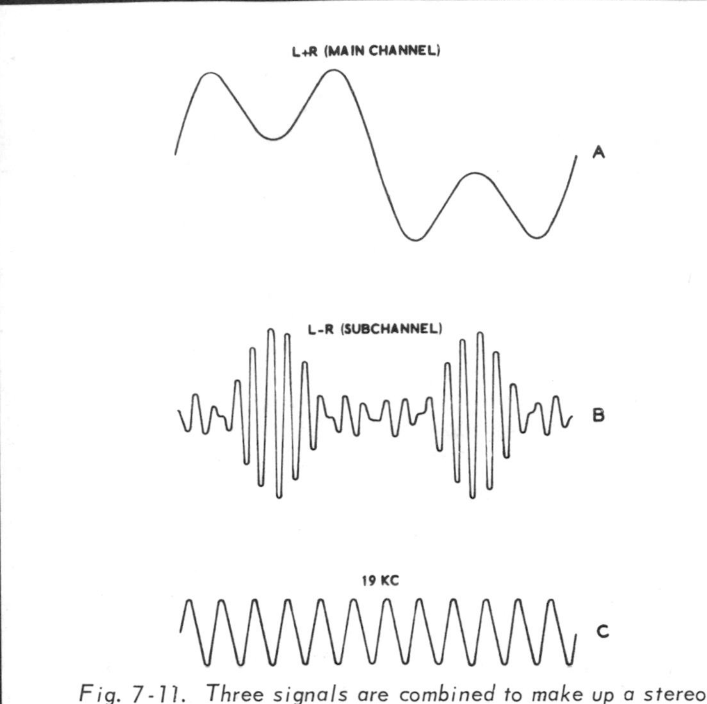


*Fig. 7-11. Three signals are combined to make up a stereo broadcast signal. Courtesy Heath Co.*

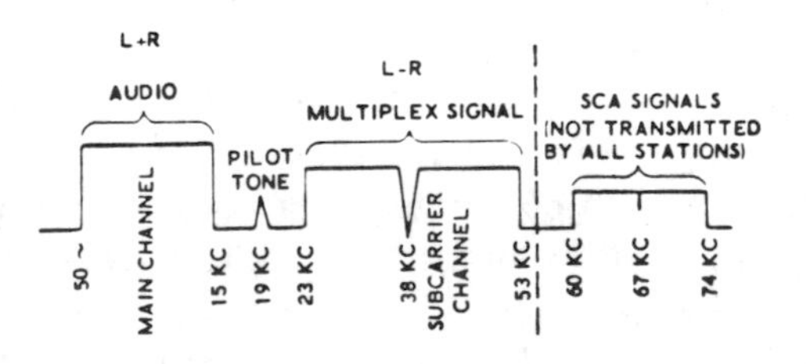


*Fig. 7-12. This chart shows the relationship of each part of a stereo signal. Courtesy Heath Co.*

C303, permits it to act as a 19-kHz amplifier, and since the output signal is taken from the emitter it functions as an emitter-follower circuit.

The 19-kHz pilot signal is amplified by Q14 and coupled from the tuned circuit to the base of 19-kHz amplifier Q23 through R350 and C337. Capacitor C338 and coil T13 form a resonant circuit in the collector of Q23. C339 and the phase-adjust control, R352, are across part of T13 so the phase of the 19-kHz output signal can be adjusted, allowing the operator to correct for any possible phase error between the 19-kHz pilot and the 38-kHz subcarrier signals which may occur between different stereo stations. This control is necessary for maximum channel separation on all stereo stations.

Two outputs are taken from the 19-kHz amplifier (Q23). One connects the 19-kHz pilot signal to the base of stereo indicator amplifier Q24 through C340. With no input signal (such as with monaural FM) only a small current flows in Q24 and the indicator does not light. When an input signal is received, Q24 begins to conduct near the positive peak of each cycle of the amplified 19-kHz pilot signal. Q24 then conducts only for short periods until the time constant of C340 and R354 allows the stage to return to its cut-off condition. The resulting pulses are shown beside the stereo indicator in Fig. 7-13 (foldout Panel F). These pulses raise the average voltage across the indicator above the 2-volt level and it lights.

### AM-FM/ FM Stereo Amplifier

The second output of 19-kHz amplifier Q23 is taken from the junction of phase control R352 and C339. The signal is coupled through C305 and R313 to the base of the 38-kHz oscillator, Q15. This stage operates only when the FM-AM selector switch is in the stereo position. Power is applied to the circuit by connecting the emitter and base resistors of Q15 to ground through terminals 1 and 15 of the mode switch.

The primary of T14 and capacitor C308 make up a tuned circuit in the collector of Q15 which is adjusted to resonate at 38 kHz. The oscillator frequency is synchronized or locked to the same frequency and phase of the originally transmitted 38-kHz subcarrier by the 19-kHz pilot signal from Q23.

Going back to the emitter-follower function of Q14, the complete FM signal is coupled from the emitter of Q14 to the SCA (and subchannel) filter circuits. When the SCA filter is on, SCA signals are removed as the complete FM signal passes through a 67-kHz parallel tuned circuit (L6 and C311). Any remaining SCA signals are shorted to ground by a 67-kHz series resonant circuit made up of C312, L5, and C313 at the output side of the 67-kHz resonant circuit.

When the SCA filter is off, all filters are bypassed and

connected directly to the next stage. The FM signal from the SCA filter circuit is coupled through C314 and R322 to the base of the emitter-follower stage (Q16). The signal from the emitter of Q16 is fed to the switching detector stage (Q17 and Q18). The switching detector circuit performs several functions simultaneously. By referring to the waveforms in Fig. 7-14 and the schematic (Fig. 7-7), we see that the FM signal (1) is coupled to the emitters of Q17 and Q18. The 38-kHz oscillator signal (2) is coupled to the bases of Q17 and Q18 through T14. When these signals are combined in this circuit, the 38-kHz carrier (which was removed at the transmitter) is reinserted into the FM signal (3). The left- and right-channel signals are then detected and coupled to separate output amplifiers as shown in Fig. 7-14.

Fig. 7-14 also shows the waveforms that are present in the switching detector circuit. Waveform (1) is the suppressed-carrier stereo FM signal that comes from Q16. Waveform (2) is the 38-kHz oscillator signal that is reinserted in the FM signal at the same phase and frequency as the original 38-kHz carrier.

The detection circuit operates as follows: When waveform (3) is applied to the switching transistors, Q18 conducts only on that part of the waveform that carries the L-channel signals. Therefore, only the L-channel appears at its output. Transistor Q17 conducts only on the R portion of the 38-kHz waveform so only the R waveform appears at its output.

In Fig. 7-15, the 38-kHz signal is shown superimposed on the stereo FM signal. At each 38-kHz peak on the L waveform, C18 conducts and Q17 is cut off. At each peak on the R waveform, Q18 is cut off and Q17 conducts. The L signal from Q18 charges C315 and is coupled through C318 to the base of Q19. The R signal charges C316 and is coupled through C317 to the base of Q20.

Q19 is the left-channel audio amplifier and post detector circuit while Q20 is used for these same functions in the right channel. Stereo balance control R332 is adjusted so equal currents flow through both Q19 and Q20. After transistors Q19 and Q20, the operation of the two channels is identical, so we will follow only the left one.

The output of Q19 is coupled through two filters, a de-emphasis network, a section of the FM-AM selector switch, and a coupling capacitor to the base of emitter-follower Q21. L8

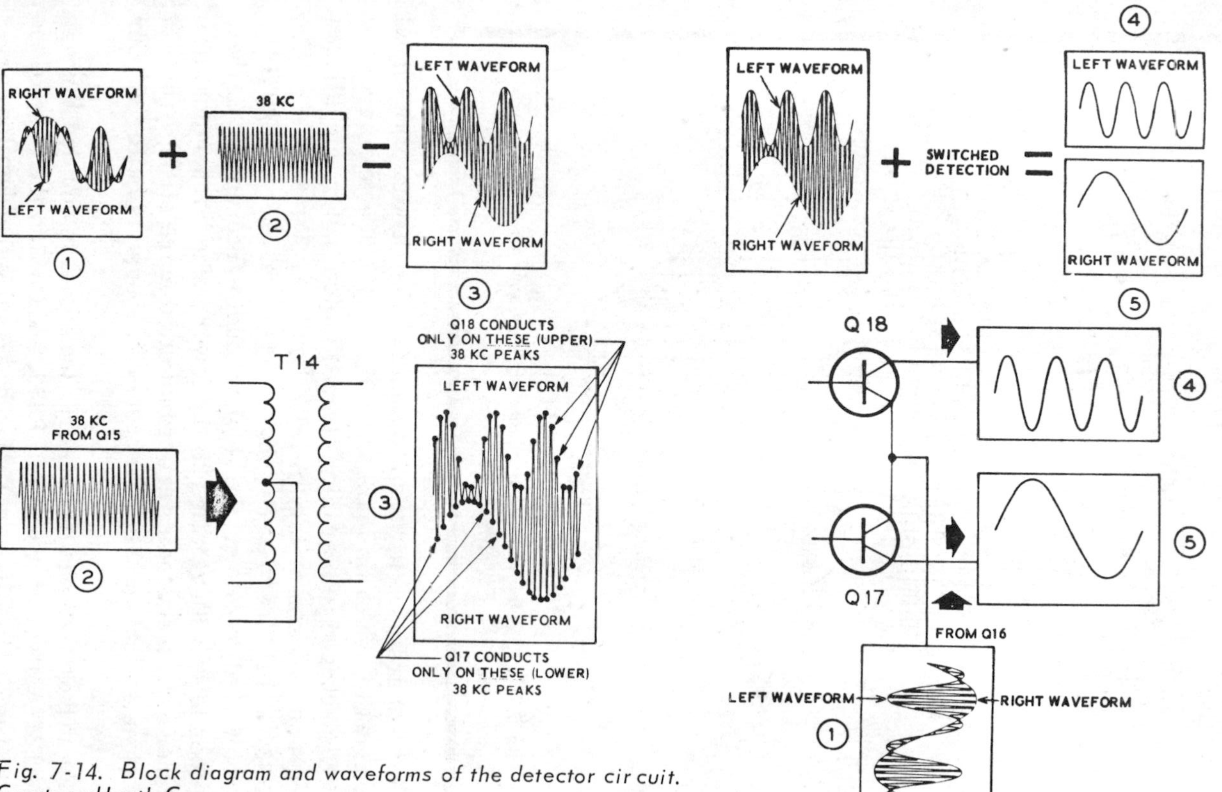


*Fig. 7-14. Block diagram and waveforms of the detector circuit. Courtesy Heath Co.*

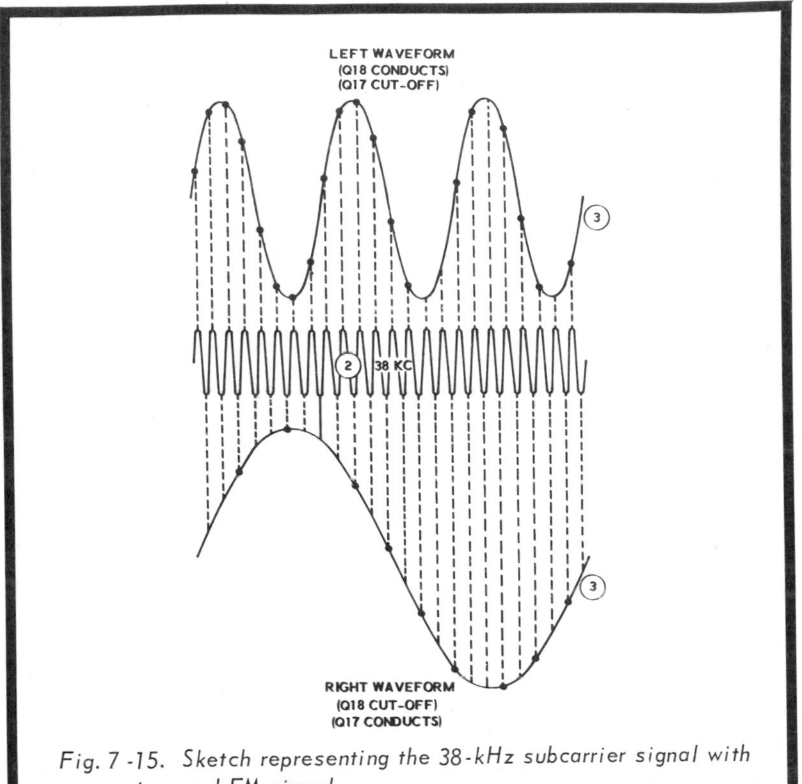


*Fig. 7-15. Sketch representing the 38-kHz subcarrier signal with a superimposed FM signal.*

and C323 are used to "trap" out any of the 19-kHz pilot signal that got through to this point. R337 and C325 are part of a PEC (packaged electronic circuit) notch filter circuit that traps out any remaining 38-kHz signal.

R337 and C327 are de-emphasis networks, a low-pass filter circuit used to return the higher audio frequencies to their proper level with relation to the lower audio frequencies. The higher audio frequencies are transmitted more strongly by FM stations so that the high-frequency response is better at your receiver.

From the de-emphasis network, the signal is coupled through the FM-AM selector switch, R339, and C331 to the base of the output emitter-follower, Q21. The signal is then applied across the left-channel level control in the emitter of Q21. From the arm of the level control the signal is coupled through C335 to the left-channel output jack.

### Monaural FM Operation

A monaural signal is coupled from the ratio detector circuit to the base of amplifier Q13 on the multiplex circuit board, and from Q13 the amplified signal is coupled to the base of Q14. Since no 19-kHz signal is present, Q14 functions only as an emitter-follower. The FM signal is then coupled through the SCA filter to emitter-follower Q16, and then to Q17 and Q18. The FM-AM selector switch disables the 38-kHz oscillator (Q15) by disconnecting the emitter and base from ground. The FM signal from Q15, therefore, is the only signal coupled to Q17 and Q18. Transistors Q17 and Q18, with no 38-kHz signal applied to them, act like any standard push-pull amplifier. The output signals from Q17 and Q18 are coupled through the audio amplifiers and output emitter-followers to the two output jacks.

### Power Supply

The power supply is shown in the schematic diagram in Fig. 7-7 (foldout Panel D). It receives AC voltage from the power line through the on-off switch, the primary of the FM line antenna, a fuse, and the primary of T11. Diodes D8 and D9 are connected in a full-wave configuration in the secondary of T11. The rectified voltage from the diodes is coupled through two filter sections consisting of R8, R9, C11, C12 and C13. A plus 14 volts is supplied to the stereo indicator circuit from the junction of R8 and R9. A regulated 9 volts is coupled from the zener diode to all other circuits. A 6.3-volt winding on T11 supplies power to the two pilot lamps.

## B/W TELEVISION RECEIVERS

A schematic diagram of a B/W television receiver is shown in Fig. 7-16 (foldout Panel G). The receiver is a portable table model with the tube filaments wired in series. The set does not have a power transformer; therefore, the tube filaments operate directly from the AC power line. As before, signals travel from left to right. The VHF and UHF tuners are shown on the schematic as two blocks labeled UHF and VHF. A schematic of the tuners is illustrated in Fig. 7-17 (foldout Panel F).

## The Tuners

The VHF tuner, consisting of V1 and V2, gets its signal from an antenna connected to terminals labeled 300 ANT INPUT. The UHF tuner uses one transistor (Q1) and has a separate antenna input since it requires a different type of antenna. In the UHF tuner, the incoming signal is coupled through a network in which C2, C4 and C14 act as the tuning capacitors for station selection. The incoming RF signal is then mixed with the signal from the UHF oscillator, Q1, before it goes to the VHF tuner through J1.

The VHF tuner receives its incoming signal from the 300-ohm antenna input, then it goes through a number of coil-capacitor networks to eliminate interference. From here the signal encounters other networks determined by the channel selector switch and is fed to the grid of V1, the RF amplifier. V1 amplifies or increases the RF signal strength and feeds it to the grid of the mixer, V2B. V2B is one-half of a dual-purpose tube; V2A is the VHF oscillator.

As mentioned earlier in our discussion of AM broadcast receivers, transmitted signals ride on an RF signal or carrier until they get to the receiver mixer stage. The mixer then combines the RF signal with an internally-generated oscillator signal to produce an IF signal. In some circuits, the mixer and oscillator may be a dual-purpose tube or transistor. In the case of a television receiver, the IF signal contains not only audio but video (picture) information as well. So V2B "mixes" the RF and oscillator signals to produce the IF signal. A switch position in the VHF tuner selects the input signal to be fed to the RF amplifier and mixer from either the VHF tuner or UHF tuner input.

## IF and Video Circuits

The IF signal (either a VHF or UHF station) is now fed from W101 to the picture or video IF stages, V203 and V204. These two stages do the same job as the IFs in any receiver: they boost the signal level. The amplifier signal at the output of V204, the 2nd IF, is now split into two parts. The video information is separated from the audio signal by video detector diode CR201 and continues on to the video output tube, V205B.

Let's follow the audio from the video detector first. Audio at the detector output goes to the grid of the sound IF tube, one-half of V201. The sound signal level is increased and coupled through transformer T202 to the grid of sound detector tube V202. The audio information from the sound detector (a ratio detector, since TV sound is FM) then goes through the volume control to the grid of the audio output tube. The volume control is used to adjust the amount of signal fed to the audio output tube which then "raises" the signal level high enough to drive the speaker.

The video signal from detector diode CR201 goes to the grid of V205B, the video output tube. A tuned circuit or "trap" in the grid circuit is used to tune out or eliminate any sound carrier which may be present before it gets to the grid. The video signal level is boosted in V205B and applied through the contrast control to the cathode of the picture tube. Also, from the output of V205B a sychronization signal, simply called "sync," is fed to the grid of the sync amplifier, V201B, and the AGC amplifier, V205A.

From the plate of V201A, the sync pulses are fed through a series of resistors and capacitors, including VERT LIN control R260, to the grid of the vertical output tube, V206A, and to the horizontal oscillator, V207. Sync pulses are used to "lock" the picture so that both the vertical and horizontal stages run in step with the incoming video signal. It does this by applying sync pulses from the received signal to the vertical oscillator and these pulses keep the vertical oscillator in step with the incoming signal. At the same time, the sync pulses are applied to the horizontal system, but not directly as in the vertical circuit.

The sync pulses (Fig. 7-16, foldout Panel G) are fed from the plate of V201B to the junction of C233 and C234, then to the horizontal phase detector made up of the diode network, SR201. This network also receives reference pulses from the horizontal circuit which are compared with the sync pulses in the phase detector. Any difference in phase between the pulses develops a correction voltage which is fed to the horizontal oscillator to put it back in step with the sync pulses.

### Vertical Circuit

The vertical circuit provides height to the TV picture by producing pulses which are used to "sweep" the electron beam in the picture tube vertically. The vertical oscillator (V206B) produces pulses which are fed to the vertical output tube (V206A). The vertical output tube amplifies these pulses and applies them through output transformer T103 to the vertical deflection coils in the yoke assembly on the picture tube neck.

### Horizontal Circuit

The horizontal circuit operates much like the vertical circuit; that is, it also produces pulses, which in this case provide width to the TV picture. The horizontal circuit also produces the pulses needed to develop the high voltage for the picture tube anode.

The horizontal oscillator (V207A) produces pulses at the rate of 15,750 per second, which are applied to the horizontal output tube (V101A) where they are amplified. The horizontal output transformer (T102) in the plate circuit of V101A drives the deflection yoke which sweeps the CRT beam horizontally. During the interval between horizontal pulses, a "flyback" pulse is fed from the yoke to the horizontal output transformer which supplies the high-voltage rectifier, V102, producing the DC voltage for the picture tube anode. In a black-and-white TV receiver the anode voltage is between 12,000 and 15,000 volts DC.

Damper tube V101B is simply used to "damp out" or prevent any undesirable oscillations in the horizontal output circuit. The damper tube is effectively connected across the horizontal coils in the yoke. One side of the yoke goes to the cathode of V101B through L103; the other side goes to the plate through L102. V101B is a diode and so it conducts only when its plate is positive with respect to its cathode. Since its plate and cathode are connected across the yoke, the direction of current flow through the yoke determines when V101B will conduct.

The TV receiver circuit shown schematically in Fig. 7-16 receives its operating voltage from a diode rectifier circuit consisting of CR101 and its filter components. Power to the circuit is applied through switch S101A.

## COLOR TV RECEIVERS

Some of the circuits in a color TV receiver, such as the tuner and audio circuits, are similar to those in the black-

and-white TV discussed previously. However, we will go into a little greater detail on these, especially where they pertain to color reception.

The schematic diagram in Fig. 7-18 (foldout Panels H and J) shows a complete color TV receiver, using both tubes and transistors. A unit of this type is commonly called a "hybrid" design. The various circuits shown within the dotted lines indicate separate circuit boards or units. This particular receiver makes use of plug-in type circuits for easier servicing. Components outside the dotted lines are normally considered to be part of the main chassis and some are found mounted on the cabinet itself. The picture tube, power supply, and most of the operating controls fall into this category. Now, let's see how this color receiver works.

### Tuner

VHF-UHF tuners are usually contained in one assembly and operate just as in a B/W TV receiver. The VHF signal is picked up by the VHF antenna, coupled through a pair of 300-ohm input terminals and various networks to the channel selector switch. The schematic shows only two of the 13-channel tuning strips in the VHF tuner. In this unit, the VHF tuner will receive Channels 2-13. When the selector switch is placed in the Channel 1 (one) position, the TV set will receive UHF signals.

Transistor Q1 is the RF amplifier, Q2 is the VHF oscillator, and Q3 is the mixer stage. VHF signals are amplified at Q1 and mixed in Q3 with the signal from the VHF oscillator (Q2) to produce a video IF output. During UHF operation (Channel 1 position) the VHF oscillator is disconnected and the UHF oscillator (Q31) is used in its place to produce video IF output to the video IF unit, ZB101.

### Video IF and AGC Unit, ZB101A

The signal from the tuner, containing video, color, and audio information, comes in to the video IF circuit (IF input jack) through a short length of coaxial cable. The signal is amplified by four video IF amplifiers, Q101 through Q104. Four amplifiers are used to provide the amount of gain and bandwidth required by this manufacturer's specifications, since this receiver is also used for more exacting industrial applications. At the output of the fourth IF stage (Q104), the video signal containing all of the video, color, and sound information is split. The video signals go through a video detector diode, D101. Tuned transformer T102 is a "trap" used to remove any audio carrier from the video signal before it goes to the video detector diode. Meanwhile, audio from the output of Q104 goes through a sound detector diode, D102, and then to the sound IF unit, ZB301A.

The video signal from the detector (D101) is fed to transistor Q106, an emitter-follower stage. In this circuit, Q106 is used to match and transfer the video signals from the detector to the contrast control and then to the video amplifier section, ZB201A.

Q106 also produces the AGC or automatic gain control signal which is amplified by Q105 and used as previously described to keep signal levels constant between weak and stronger stations. AGC circuits normally provide either a "forward" or "reverse" bias. This receiver uses both types. "Reverse" AGC is applied to the bases of the first two video IF stages, Q101 and Q102. At the same time, reverse AGC is amplified and inverted by Q4 and fed to the tuner as "forward" AGC.

### Video Amplifier and Sync Unit

The video signal from the IF unit goes through contrast control VR45 to the video amplifier unit, ZB201A, and the base of Q201, the first video amplifier. From the collector of Q201, the video signal is fed through a delay line, L203, to the base of Q202. The signal then goes to the grid of the video output tube, V201, where it is further amplified. The signal from V201 is then fed as the luminance signal to the cathodes of the three-gun color picture tube.

Also from the contrast control, video signal is fed to Q203 and Q204. These transistors make up the first color or "chroma" and sync amplifiers. They are connected in a circuit arrangement called a "Darlington pair." Diode D201 and transistor Q205 act as sync levelers before the signal is fed to sync separator transistor Q206. The blanking amplifier, Q207, together with diodes D203, 204, and 205, shape the horizontal and vertical blanking pulses from the deflection circuits and pass them on to the cathode of V201.

## Chroma Oscillator Unit, ZB701

The chroma or color signal from the output of the video sync unit (pin 3 of ZB201A) is coupled through L701 to the base of emitter-follower transistor Q701. The emitter-follower circuit is often used in transistorized units to match a high-impedance input to a low-impedance output. In this case, the emitter-follower matches the input of the video sync unit to the low-impedance color control, VR46. The color control applies signal to the base of Q702. Here, the signal is further amplified and fed through bandpass transformer T701 to the chroma demodulators in the chroma output unit, ZB751A.

Meanwhile, V701, the burst amplifier tube, is turned on during color burst time by a pulse from the horizontal output transformer (T41). The amplified burst signal is then coupled through T702 to diodes D701 and 702. These diodes are the automatic phase detectors and their output signal is fed to the chroma oscillator, V702, to keep it locked in sync with the burst signal. When a burst signal is present, diode D703 develops a negative voltage which biases off the color killer transistor, Q703. When there is no color signal, Q703 conducts and cuts off Q702, the chroma amplifier.

## Chroma Output Unit

The chroma output circuit, ZB751A, receives the chroma and chroma oscillator signals from ZB701, the chroma oscillator circuit, through pins 1, 3, and 4. These two signals are applied to the balanced demodulator diodes, D751 752, 753, and 754. The demodulator diodes separate the colors. Their outputs are the B-Y (blue minus yellow) and R-Y (red minus yellow) signals. These two signals are then fed directly to amplifiers Q751 and Q752 and the red and blue sections of V751. We can see this on the schematic by following the connections to the grids (pin 8 and pin 10) of V751.

Green is produced by mixing the red and blue signals and then amplifying it in its own section of V751. The amplified chroma signals—red, green, and blue—are then fed to the grids of the color picture tube, pins 3, 7, and 12.

## 4.5 MHz Sound IF Amplifier

The sound detector, D102, in the video IF unit applies a signal to the sound IF amplifier, ZB301A, through pin 5. The audio or sound signal is fed through a tuned transformer, T301, to the base of Q301, a 4.5-MHz sound amplifier. The signal is amplified and fed to a limiter-amplifier (Q302) and then through a tuned transformer (T302) to the ratio-detector diodes D301 and 302. The audio output from the diodes is fed through the volume control, VR47, to the audio amplifier unit, ZB401A.

### Audio Amplifier

The audio amplifier used in this TV chassis is quite conventional. The signal from the volume control is applied through a coupling capacitor, C401, to the base of Q401. This transistor, along with Q402, forms a "Darlington pair" circuit which we described earlier. These two transistors are then used to "drive" or feed a Class "B" output stage, Q403 and Q404, which in turn provides sufficient audio to drive the 16-ohm speaker. An optional earphone output is also available in this particular chassis. When the earphone is used, it automatically opens the speaker circiut which is connected through a closed-circuit earphone jack. The earphone then replaces the speaker as the load on the audio output stage.

### Vertical Deflection Unit

There are two deflection systems in any TV set, one which produces a vertical sweep and one to produce horizontal sweep. Together they cause the picture to fill the screen from top to bottom (vertically) and from left to right (horizontally). Without deflection, our picture would be nothing more than a dot in the middle of the picture tube.

The vertical deflection unit, ZB601A, consists of a multivibrator-amplifier tube, V601, and associated components shown within the dotted lines, plus a vertical output transformer, T42, which is not mounted on the vertical circuit board itself. V601 produces pulses which it also amplifies and feeds through T42 to the deflection yoke assembly, Y41. The output from the vertical transformer is connected to the deflection yoke through pin 2 or socket SO41.

### Horizontal Deflection Unit

The horizontal deflection system (ZB501A) also receives a sync pulse from the output of the video amplifier unit, ZB201A, which is fed to a dual-diode phase detector, DD501. These diodes develop a control voltage for the horizontal multivibrator tube, V501.

The output of V501 is fed to the grid of the horizontal output tube, V502, which is connected to the horizontal output transformer, T41. Like the vertical output transformer, T41 is mounted on the main chassis rather than on the circuit board.

The horizontal system also provides pulses used to develop high-voltage on the picture tube anode. In color receivers, this voltage is normally close to 25,000 volts! The high voltage in this circuit is regulated or controlled by taking a reference voltage from the B-plus boost line and using it to control the regulator transistor, Q501. Diodes D501 and D502 in the base circuit of Q501 help to regulate the high voltage by shaping the driving waveform or signal at the grid of V502, which in turn controls V502's output plate current. The plate of V502 is connected to T41.

## Horizontal Efficiency Unit

The horizontal efficiency section (ZB551) contains a diode called the "damper," D551. This diode operates with the horizontal efficiency coil, L551, to adjust the cathode current of the 6JE6 horizontal output tube (V502). L551 actually "tunes" the horizontal output circuit.

The high-voltage rectifier tube, 3A3A, receives high-voltage pulses from the horizontal deflection system through output transformer T41. The cathode of the rectifier connects to the picture tube anode.

## Power Supply

The power supply is mounted on the main chassis and consists of two separate full-wave rectifiers. The AC line voltage is connected through a 3-amp circuit breaker, CB41, to the primary of the power transformer, TM41. The secondary of TM41 has four windings; two are used for the rectifier circuits. SR41 and SR42, with the filter choke and filter capacitors, produce the plus 300-volt supply for the tubes. SR43 and SR44, with their filter components, provide the low DC voltage for the transistor circuits.

## Convergence Board

This unit is shown within a dotted circle (ZB801). A convergence assembly consists of a network of coils, capacitors, and resistors used to provide a slight amount of control over vertical and horizontal deflection of the CRT electron beams. When all controls are properly adjusted, the CRT beams will coincide to produce accurate color register. The coils of this assembly are mounted on the picture tube neck, as are the controls in this model. In some color receivers, the controls and convergence board components are cabled to the color yoke coil assembly. In others, the convergence board is mounted separate from the yoke and cabled to it.

# CHAPTER 8

# Specialized Equipment Schematics

"Intercoms" are used in many homes, factories, and offices to allow people to communicate back and forth much like a telephone but without the use of telephone lines. The schematic of one such intercom, a wireless type, is shown in Fig. 8-1 (foldout Panel L). It is "wireless" because it uses no other wiring other than the AC power line.

The intercom has a transmitter, receiver, and a common power supply. Referring to the schematic, when the intercom is operated as a receiver, a signal from another intercom is picked up by coils L1, L2B, and series capacitor C4, which form a tuned circuit. When the channel switch is in the "high" position, the circuit is tuned to 220 kHz. In the "low" position, capacitor C3 is put in the circuit and the frequency is lowered to 180 kHz. Of course, to communicate with another station or stations all intercom units must be on the same frequency. The received signal is coupled from L2B to L2D, through R3 and C6 to amplifier transistor X1. From X1 the signal is coupled through T1 to diode D2. This circuit removes either the 220- or 180-kHz signal and leaves just the audio.

The audio circuits closely resemble those in a small AM radio in many respects. The audio is fed to volume control R9, which is used to set the amount of signal fed to transistor X3. From X3 the audio is further amplified by X4 and fed to the speaker through T2.

Transistor X2 is a squelch circuit which is connected to X3; it turns off X2 when no signal is received. This eliminates any noise or background hash when no signals are coming in. Control R25 sets the squelch operating or triggering level.

When the intercom is used to send a signal, transistors X2, X3, and X4 operate as audio amplifiers and transistor X1 operates as an oscillator and RF stage. The operator talks into the speaker and his voice is amplified by X2, X3, and X4. The amplified signal goes to coil L2A and then to oscillator stage X1. The oscillator operates at a frequency of either 220 or 180 kHz and is modulated by the audio. Coils L2A and L2B then couple the signal to the AC power line and it is picked up by another receiver.

The power supply is a conventional full-wave diode bridge circuit. As shown by the dotted lines around the diodes, it is a composite unit. When transmitting, resistors R26 and R27 are connected in parallel to provide a higher DC output voltage. The fuse link in this unit is a length of number 39 or 40 wire connected between lugs two and three of line coil L1.

The intercom circuit in Fig. 8-2 (foldout Panel M) uses wires between units to carry the signals. This is a master station designed to operate with other master remote stations.

## SSB AMATEUR TRANSCEIVER

A single-sideband (SSB) amateur transceiver is shown schematically in Fig. 8-3 (foldout Panel N) and as a block diagram in Fig. 8-4 (foldout Panel O). We will refer to both during our "tour" of the circuits. As the block diagram shows, the unit is divided into two main sections–the receiver and transmitter. Some sections are used for both transmit and receive as indicated on the block diagram.

The microphone input to the transmitter is applied at the jack labeled MIC INPUT which connects the audio to speech amplifier V1A, one-half of a 6EA8 tube. The audio is fed to the grid of V1A, and the ground pin on the mic connector is connected to ground by the pushbutton on the mic itself. As shown on the schematic, this pin is also connected to the grid of the relay amplifier (V12B) to ground it when the mic push-to-talk switch is depressed. This tube then activates the transmit relays.

The amplified audio from the plate of V1A is coupled through C9 to the "microphone level" section of the MIC/CW LEVEL control and also to the VOX (voice-operated relay) amplifier circuit. The microphone level control sets the amount of modulation because it adjusts the speech signal level through cathode-follower V1B to the balanced modulator circuit. For LSB (lower sideband) and USB (upper sideband) operation, the V1B grid resistor, R12, is returned to ground through wafer 1F on the mode switch and contacts 6 and 10 of relay RL2. When the mode switch is in the "tune" or "CW" position, the cathode follower (V1B) is cut off by a bias voltage from divider resistors R308 and R309.

The carrier oscillator, actually two crystal oscillators, supplies an RF signal to the balanced modulator for transmit operation. It also provides a heterodyne signal to the product detector stage, V13, during receive. V16A and crystal V1 serve as the USB carrier oscillator and V16B with crystals Y2 and Y3 act as the LSB and CW carrier oscillator.

The desired carrier oscillator (V16B) for the transmitted frequency is placed in operation by wafer 1R of the mode switch which connects its plate circuit to B-plus. Wafer 2R connects the proper crystal to the grid of V16B. When the mode switch is in the CW position, B-plus is connected through part of relay RL1 to either V16A or V16B.

When receiving CW signals, lugs 1 and 9 of relay RL1 place V16B and crystal Y1 in operation. For transmitting CW, lugs 5 and 9 of relay RL1 place V16B and crystal Y3 in operation. When receiving CW signals, the receiver is automatically tuned 1 kHz below the incoming signal. The incoming signal "beats" with the transceiver beat-frequency oscillator signal (V16B and crystal Y1). When transmitting, V16B and crystal Y3 keep the transceiver output at the same frequency as the incoming signal from the other station.

### Balanced Modulator

Diodes CR1, CR2, CR3, and CR4 are connected in a ring-type balanced modulator circuit. When an audio signal from V1B and the RF signal from carrier oscillator V16 are fed to the balanced modulator, two additional frequencies are produced: one is equal to the sum of the audio and carrier frequencies and the other is equal to the difference between them. These sum and difference frequencies are the upper and lower sideband signals, and these are the only signals that appear at the output of the balanced modulator circuit.

When no audio is received at the input, the carrier signal from V16 is balanced out by the CARRIER NULL control so there is no output from T1. When an audio signal does come into the diodes from V1B, it upsets this balanced condition and an RF signal appears at the secondary of T1 This signal is then coupled through C22 to isolation amplifier V2. The secondary of T1 is tuned to the CW carrier frequency.

## Isolation Amplifier

Both the upper and lower sideband signals from the balanced modulator circuit are fed to the cathode of the isolation amplifier (V2) through C22. As suggested by the name, V2 isolates the balanced modulator from the crystal filter and provides the proper impedance match to the crystal filter. The gain of this amplifier is varied by the ALC (automatic level control) voltage applied to its cathode through resistors R21 and R22. (The complete ALC circuit is described later under that heading).

During transmit, the output of V2 is coupled through C506 to the crystal filter. In the CW mode of operation the gain of V2 is controlled by the CW section of the MIC/CW LEVEL control which applies a variable negative bias to the grid of V2 through wafer 1R of the mode switch, R21, and R22. B-plus voltage is supplied to the screen of V2 in the transmit mode only through R937 and terminals 7 and 11 of RL2.

## Crystal Filters

Crystal filter FL1 has a center frequency of 3395 kHz and a usable bandwidth of 2.1 kHz. In the LSB mode the filter passes only the sum frequencies which contain the upper sideband information. In the USB mode, only the difference frequencies containing the lower sideband information are passed. The actual RF carrier frequency itself is attenuated by the crystal filter. This attenuation, plus the attenuation of the balanced modulator, equals approximately 50 db.

## IF Amplifier

The signal from the output of the crystal filter is fed to IF amplifier V3. The second IF amplifier (V4) is not used during transmit. The output from V3 is coupled through C111 to the grid of the first transmitter mixer stage, V5A. The 6.8-MHz trap is used to remove the second harmonic of the 3.395 MHz signal. (3.395 plus 3.395 is 6.8). Transformer T102 is used as the plate load for V3, and it couples signal to V4 when the unit is in the receive mode.

ALC voltage is applied through lugs 8 and 12 of relay RL2 to the grid of V3 to provide automatic level control for the transmitted signal. When the mode switch is in the CW and TUNE positions, the gain of V3 is controlled by a DC bias from the arm of the MIC/CW LEVEL control through wafer 1R of the mode switch and terminals 8 and 12 of RL2.

### LMO/ Crystal Oscillators

If the transceiver is to operate on the 3.5- to 4-MHz band, the first mixer tube (V5A) has to produce an 8.5-MHz output signal. This signal is obtained by mixing the 3.395-MHz IF signal at the grid of V5A with the oscillator signal which is applied to its cathode from the FREQ control switch. The FREQ control switch receives signals from the LMO (linear master oscillator) or from V5B. The LMO is a stable, variable oscillator which can be continuously tuned over a frequency range of 5 to 5.5 MHz. Crystal-controlled oscillator V5B may be switched into the circuit in place of the LMO for crystal-controlled operation of the transceiver if desired.

The FREQ control switch does several things: in the LMO position the signal from the LMO is connected to the first transmitter mixer (V5A) and to the first receiver mixer (V11). In the LOCKED AUX position, the output of crystal-oscillator V5B is connected to V5A and to the second receiver mixer, V12A. In the UNLOCKED AUX position, the output of V5B is connected to V5A and the LMO output is connected to V12A. The term "locked" means that the receiver and transmitter sections are controlled by a common oscillator, which places them on identical frequencies. The "unlocked" position means that the transmitter and receiver are controlled by separate oscillators and their frequencies may differ.

### First Transmitter Mixer

The 3.395-MHz IF signal at the grid and the 5.105-MHz signal (or crystal-oscillator signal) at the cathode are mixed in the first transmitter mixer tube (V5A) to produce sum and difference frequencies. The 8.5-MHz sum of these two signals is coupled from the plate of V5A through bandpass filter T202 to the second transmitter mixer, V6. The bandpass filter is tuned to pass only those signals between 8.395 and 8.895 MHz. All other signals are attenuated. Only the sum of the IF and LMO signals falls within this range, so it is the only frequency range passed on to the second mixer.

First mixer V5A, second mixer V6, and driver V7 are cut off during the receive mode by a negative grid voltage applied through D301 and R301. This voltage is removed during transmit by lugs 6 and 10 of relay RL2, which grounds the cathode side of D301.

### Heterodyne Oscillator and Cathode Follower

The heterodyne oscillator, V19A, operates as a tuned-plate crystal oscillator. The proper plate coil for each band, L601 through L608, is selected by wafer 2F on the band switch. The output signal from the plate of V19A is coupled through cathode-follower V19B to the cathode of V6 and to the cathode of the first receiver mixer, V11. The correct oscillator crystal for each band is selected by wafer 1R of the band switch. Crystals below 20 MHz are fundamentals and the higher frequency crystals operate on their third overtone. The grid of V19A can be monitored at TP to check oscillator operation.

### Second Transmitter Mixer

The 8.5-MHz signal from the first transmitter mixer and bandpass filter is coupled to the grid of V6. The 12.395-MHz output from the heterodyne oscillator is also coupled to the grid of V6. These signals are mixed to produce the operating frequency. The frequency of the tuned plate circuit of V6 is the operating frequency and all others are shorted to ground.

In this case, the difference between the 8.5-MHz input signal and the 12.395-MHz heterodyne oscillator frequency results in a mixer output of 3.895-MHz which is then coupled to the grid of V7. The 3.5-MHz plate tuning coil, L701, is connected across the tuned plate circuit on all bands, along with the fixed and variable tuning capacitors. Band switch wafer 3F connects the correct amount of inductance in parallel with L701 to tune each band, except the 3.5-MHz band which uses coil L701 only. Tuning capacitor C421B is connected across the tuned circuit on all bands. Tuning capacitor C421A is connected in parallel with C421B on the 80-meter band only by band switch wafer 3R.

### Driver

Driver stage V7 amplifies the 3.895-MHz signal from the second transmitter mixer (V6) to a level high enough to drive the final amplifiers. The 3.5-MHz plate tuning coil, L801, is connected across the tuned plate circuit on all bands, along with the fixed and variable tuning capacitors. A secondary (link) winding on L801 is used in the receive mode to couple the received signal to the transceiver. Band switch wafer 4F connects the correct amount of inductance in parallel with L801 to tune each band, except the 3.5-MHz (80-meter) band which uses only L801. Band switch wafer 4R connects additional capacitance in parallel with C422B for the 80-meter (3.5 MHz), 40-meter (7 MHz) and 20-meter (14 MHz) bands. V7 is neutralized by feeding a portion of the plate signal back to the grid through a "neutralizing wire" capacitor to the tuned plate circuit of the second transmitter mixer.

### Final Amplifiers

Final amplifiers V8 and V9 are connected in parallel and function as Class AB1 linears. A fixed negative bias is applied to their grids through R916 and L903. A steady fixed bias is needed to limit zero-signal plate current. B-plus is removed from the screen grids during receive by terminals 7 and 11 of RL2 to reduce the plate current to zero and cut the tubes off. RF driving voltage is developed across RF choke L903.

During LSB and USB operation, the driving voltage is controlled by the MIC/CW LEVEL control in the grid of V1B and by the limiting section of the ALC voltage. The ALC voltage is fed back to the isolation amplifier (V2) and IF amplifier V3. The output from V8 and V9 is coupled through RF parasitic chokes L904 and L902 and capacitor C915 to the final tuning capacitor, C925, and capacitor C915 to the final tuning capacitor, C925, to the plate tank coils L905 and L906. The parasitic chokes are used to eliminate any tendency toward unwanted VHF oscillations. Wafer 5R of the band switch connects the proper portion of the plate tank coil in the circuit for each band by shorting out the unused sections. Wafer 5R also selects the proper combination of final tank tuning and loading capacitors for each band.

Neutralization of the final amplifier is accomplished by feeding a portion of the plate signal back to the grid through neutralizing capacitors C913 and C914 and across C801 in a bridge circuit. The output signal from the final tank coil is coupled through lugs 8 and 12 of RL1 to the RF OUT connector. The antenna switch allows the use of separate antennas for receive and transmit if desired.

### ALC Circuit

The ALC bias voltage is developed by a small sample of the signal in the final amplifier. This signal is rectified, filtered, and fed back to the preceding stages to adjust gain automatically as needed, much like the AGC circuits described in the receiver circuits. ALC assures maximum transmitter output without overloading.

ALC for the transmitter is developed in the TALC (Triple Action Level Control) circuit. This circuit keeps the transmitter from overloading, without causing the voice peaks to be flat-topped, by compressing the speech waveform. The rectified voltage from D903 is applied to an RC network consisting of R914, R915, C931, and C932. This network filters the DC bias voltage which is fed back to the preceding stages and allows it to build up quickly and decay slowly. From the RC filter network, the ALC voltage is applied to the grid of isolation amplifier V2 where it limits the output, thus reducing the drive to the final amplifiers. The ALC voltage is also coupled to IF amplifier V3 through terminals 8 and 12 of RL2. ALC voltage is not developed for CW operation. An adjustable bias from the MIC/CW LEVEL control is used instead.

### Tone Oscillator and Amplifier

Tone oscillator V15 generates a 1000-Hz audio signal that is used only for CW operation. This tone is inserted into the VOX circuit to turn the transmitter on. It also couples to the receiver audio amplifier so the operator can use it to monitor his own transmitted signal. The tone oscillator is turned on when its cathode is connected to ground through wafer 2F of the mode switch. The frequency of V15A is determined by a phase-shift network in its grid circuit. The phase-shift network is a packaged or encapsulated unit.

From the plate of V15A the 1000-Hz tone is coupled through C315 and R329 to the grid of tone amplifier V15B. V15B is normally cut off by a negative bias at its grid from the junction of R311 and R312. When the CW key is closed, cut-off bias is removed and V15B conducts. From the plate of V15B the 1000-Hz tone is coupled to the CW tone volume control and then to audio amplifier V14B. The 1000-Hz tone is also coupled through C313 and R328 to the grid of the VOX amplifier (V17A) which causes the transmitter to turn on.

## CW Operation

Assume the mode switch is in the CW position. The cathode follower (V1B) is cut off and the arm of the VOX SENSITIVITY control is grounded so stray microphone signals do not reach the balanced modulator or VOX circuits. The CW crystal, Y3, is connected to the grid of carrier oscillator V16B and the balanced modulator circuit is unbalanced so it will produce an output signal. The transmitted CW signal then passes through either the "accessory CW filter" or the SSB filter. The drive to the final amplifiers is controlled by the CW section of the MIC/CW LEVEL control, which adjusts the bias of isolation amplifier V2 and IF amplifier V3. Cut-off bias is applied to the grids of transmitter mixers V5A and V6 and to the grid of driver amplifier V7 through mode switch wafer 1F and diode D904. Tone oscillator V15A is turned on.

When the key is closed the 100-Hz tone signal is coupled to the VOX circuit where it causes the relays to be switched to the transmit position. The relays stay in this position for a length of time that is determined by the setting of the VOX DELAY control. At the same time, the key shorts out the cut-off bias that is applied to the transmitter mixer stages and to the driver amplifier stage, allowing them to conduct and place the transmitter on the air.

The RF output signal from CW carrier oscillator V16B is coupled to the balanced modulator stage. The unbalanced condition of this stage causes the RF signal to be coupled through transformer T1 to isolation amplifier V2. From V2 the signal goes through the transmitter in the same manner as the LSB and USB signals.

### Switching

Fig. 8-5 shows the position and assigns an identifying number to each of the relay sections on the main schematic. The numbers used in the following paragraphs explain how each section is used.

1. This section applies B-plus to the correct half of carrier oscillator tube V16 in the TUNE and CW positions of the mode switch.

2. These contacts are connected to the power circuit to supply AC power to operate external linear amplifiers and other devices. The contacts have a rating of 3 amperes at 117v AC or 30v DC.

3. B-plus voltage is applied through these contacts to the screens of V2, V7, V8, and V9 in the transmit mode and to the screens of V4, V10, and V11 in the receive mode.

4. These contacts ground the receiver cut-off bias in the receive mode. In the transmit mode they ground the cut-off bias that is applied through diode D301 to transmitter stages V5A, V6, and V7.

5. In the transmit mode, these relay contacts apply ALC voltage (or CW bias) to the grid of V3. In the receive mode they apply AVC voltage to V3.

6. This section applies 150v B-plus through the FREQ control switch to either the LMO or crystal oscillator V5B.

7. Two sets of contacts are used to switch the antenna between the receive and transmit circuits.

When in the transmit mode, a large negative bias (approximately -90 volts) is applied through the RF gain control and diode D905 to the grids of RF amplifier V10 and first re-

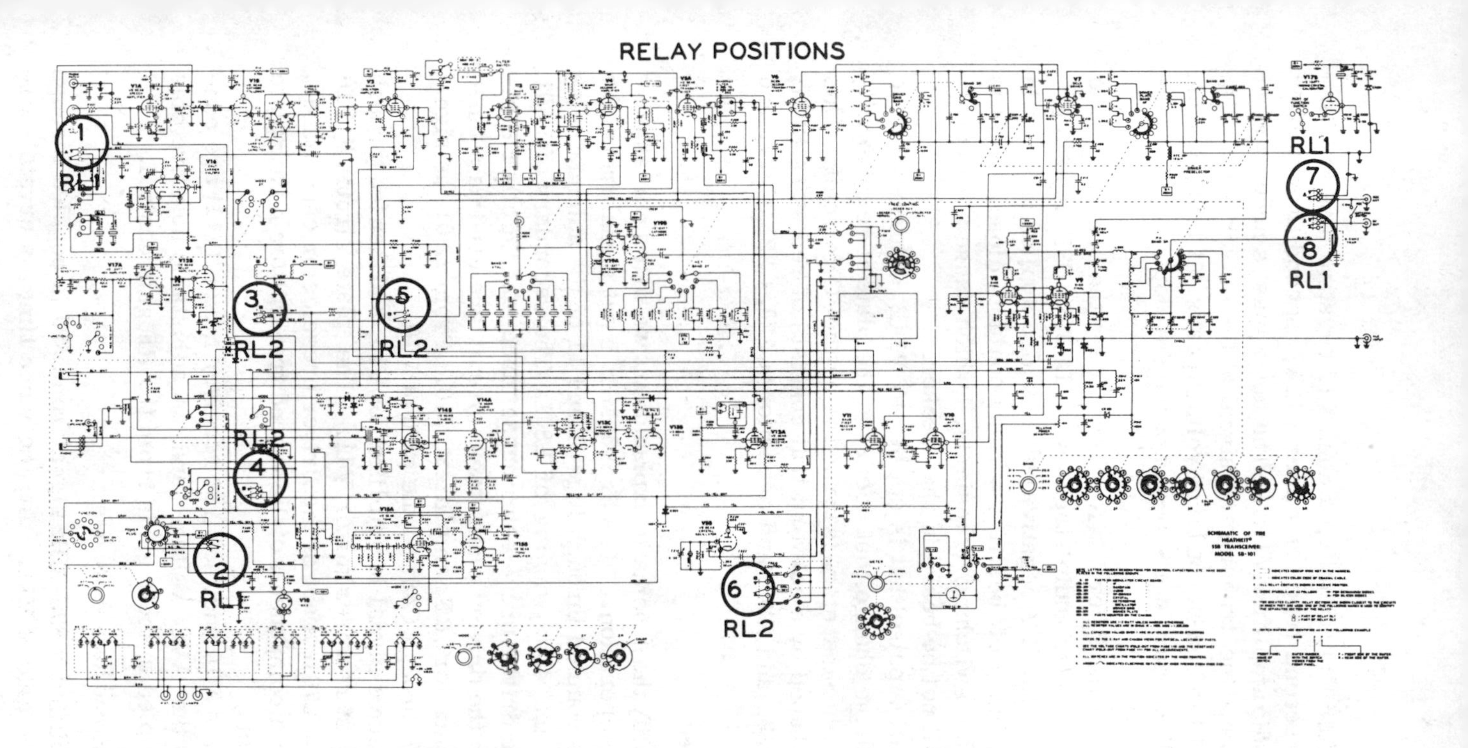


Fig. 8-5. Schematic showing positions of the relay switch sections on the SSB receiver schematic (Fig. 8-3). Courtesy Heath Co.

ceiver mixer V11. Smaller amounts of negative bias are also applied to second receiver mixer V12A, second IF amplifier V4, and audio amplifier V14A. The large bias is necessary at V10 to keep the transmitter signal at the driver plate from causing V10 to conduct on large voltage peaks. (If this happens, spikes will appear at the peaks of the envelope on the transmitted signal.)

First audio amplifier V14A is cut off by the bias voltage to quiet the receiver audio stages when LSB or USB signals are being transmitted. A negative pulse is also applied to the grid of V14A to cut it off before the relay contacts close. This is done so the switching transients, which cause a "popping" sound, will not be heard in the speaker.

The negative pulse that is applied to V14B is formed by the sudden voltage change that occurs at the plate of relay amplifier V12B when that stage is turned on by the VOX circuit. This pulse is shaped by a network that consists of resistors R337, R338, R339, and R340 and capacitors C320, C321, C322, and C323.

### RF Amplifier

To simplify the schematic explanation, we will again assume 80-meter operation. The 3.895-MHz input signal from the antenna is coupled through lugs 3 and 11 of the antenna relay (RL1) to the link winding of L801. The secondary of L801, part of the driver preselector capacitance, and the other components in the driver plate tank circuit are used as a tuned input circuit for RF amplifier V10. From L801 the signal is coupled through C408 to the grid of V10.

The received signal is amplified by V10, and then fed through C419 to first receiver mixer V11. The plate circuit if V10 consists of L701, part of the driver preselector capacitance, and the other components of the second transmitter mixer plate tank circuit.

The gain of V10 and the first receiver mixer (V11) are controlled by the AVC voltage and an adjustable negative bias that is coupled to their grids from the RF gain control.

### First and Second Receiver Mixers

The amplified 3.895-MHz signal from V10 is coupled through C419 to the grid of V11. At the same time, a crystal-controlled 12.395-MHz signal is coupled to the V11 cathode from V19B the heterodyne oscillator cathode-follower. These two signals are mixed together in V11 and coupled, with the sum and difference frequencies, to the bandpass filter. The bandpass filter, which passes only the frequencies between 8.395 and 8.895 MHz, allows the 8.5-MHz difference frequency to pass on from V11 to the grid of the second mixer tube (V12A).

A 5.105-MHz signal is coupled from either the LMO or crystal oscillator V5B through the FREQ control switch to the V12A cathode. The 8.5-MHz signal at the grid and the 5.105-MHz signal at the cathode are then mixed together in V12A and the 3.395-MHz difference frequency is coupled through crystal filter FL1 to the IF amplifiers.

The filter switch selects either crystal filter FL1 for SSB use or FL2 for CW use. Crystal filter FL1 sets the IF bandwidth at 2.1 kHz wide. This narrow, steep-sided passband permits good selectivity for SSB reception in crowded amateur bands. Crystal filter FL2 can be switched in for CW reception. FL2 sets the IF bandwidth at 400 Hz. This narrow bandwidth is good for CW reception only.

### IF Amplifiers

The signal from FL1 is fed through capacitor C101 to the first IF amplifier (V3). The amplified signal from V3 is coupled to the grid of V5A, which is cut off during receive, and to the second IF amplifier (V4) through IF transformer T102. The amplified signal from V4 is coupled through IF transformer T103 to the product detector, V13C. The same signal is also coupled through C112 to the plate of the AVC rectifier, V13B. Supply voltage for the screen of V4 is switched through lugs 3 and 11 of RL2. AVC voltage is supplied to the grid of V4 by the AVC line. AVC voltage is switched to the grid of V3 through lugs 4 and 12 of RL2.

### AVC Circuit

The negative bias determines the amount of amplification that will be obtained from RF amplifier V10, first receiver mixer V11, and IF amplifiers V3 and V4. The DC bias for these stages comes from two sources: the negative DC voltage at the arm of the RF gain Control, and from the AVC voltage. These two voltage sources are connected to diodes D101 and D905, together acting as a "gate" which permits either bias voltage to control the gain of V10, V11, etc., without interacting with each other.

From the diode junction the bias voltage is coupled through R412 to the grids of V10 and V11 and through resistor R415 to the grids of V3 and V4. Voltage-divider resistors R415 and R416 allow only one half of the total bias voltage to be applied to the grids of V3 and V4.

AVC voltage is obtained by coupling part of the IF signal through C112 to AVC diodes V13A and V13B. These diodes produce a negative DC voltage at pin 1 of V13A that is proportional to the signal strength. This negative voltage is developed across R124, R117, C110 and C124. Capacitor C124 charges quickly to the peak voltage so the AVC responds quickly to prevent distortion in V3, V4, V10 and V11 when strong signals are received. Capacitor C110 charges more slowly, and keeps the AVC voltage proportional to the average level of the received signal. This produces a fast-attack slow-release AVC characteristic.

An incoming signal that produces a negative AVC voltage significantly higher than the bias voltage from the RF gain control reduces the gain of V10, V11, V3, and V4. This holds the output of the RF and IF amplifier stages at a nearly constant level despite wide changes in the received signal level.

### Product Detector

The 3.395-MHz signal from IF amplifier V4 is coupled to the grid of product detector V13C. At the same time, the signal from carrier oscillator V16 is fed to the cathode of V13C (3.3936 MHz for the lower sideband or 3.3964 MHz for the upper sideband). These two signals are then mixed in V13C, resulting in an audio output signal which is the difference frequency between these two signals. Capacitors C119 and C121 and resistor R119 form a filter network that bypasses any RF signal at the V13C plate to ground but permits the audio signal to pass through to audio amplifier V14A.

### Audio and Power Amplifier

The signal from the product detector is applied to the AF gain control to determine the amount of signal that will be coupled through C308 to the grid of V14A. The audio signal is amplified in V14A and fed to power amplifier V14B. V14B supplies the audio power through output transformer T301 to the output connectors. Capacitor C928 couples a portion of the output back to the cathode of V14B as negative feedback to reduce distortion.

Three outputs are provided by tranformer T301: a headphone output, a 600-ohm output, and an 8-ohm speaker output. Audio power to the 8-ohm speaker jack is rated at 2 watts maximum. An audio signal is also supplied to the anti-trip network from the plate of V14B.

#### Crystal Calibrator

Crystal-calibrator stage V17B is connected as a Pierce crystal oscillator. When the functionswitch is placed in the "calibrate" position, the cathode of V17B is grounded and an accurate 100-kHz signal is connected through C218 and CR201 to the receiver antenna input. The harmonics of this signal are then used for dial calibration checks. Calibrate crystal capacitor C220 may be adjusted to set the crystal calibrator to exactly 100-kHz using some standard such as WWV.

The "calibrate" position of the function switch also connects the grid of VOXamplifier V17A to ground to avoid accidentally energizing the transmitter when using the crystal calibrator.

#### Metering Circuits

For the transmitting mode of operation, there are five different settings of the meter switch: final grid current, final plate current, ALC voltage, relative power output, and high voltage. In the ALC position, in the receive mode, the circuit operates as an S meter.

To measure the grid current at final amplifiers V8 and V9, the meter is shunted across R916 in the common grid circuit. The meter will then read from 0 to 1 ma of grid current. To measure final amplifier plate current, the meter is connected between the final cathodes and ground in parallel with the cathode resistors. Plate current is read on the 0 to 500 ma range of the meter.

To measure ALC voltage, the meter is connected between the cathode and screen circuits of IF amplifier V3. The meter-zero control is adjusted for zero current flow through the meter with no signal input. When V3 receives a signal, the resulting current fluctuations in the cathode are indicated on the meter. Since the ALC voltage at the grid controls the gain of V3, the cathode current of V3 gives a relative indication of the ALC voltage level.

For relative power measurements, a small portion of the transmitter output signal is developed across R912, rectified by CR901, and filtered by C933. The resulting DC voltage is then indicated by the meter. The "relative power" sensitivity control allows the operator to set his full power output indication at a convenient meter reading.

The high voltage is brought down to a measurable level by a precision multiplier resistor, R921; thus, 0-1000 volts can be read on the 0-10 scale of the meter. Resistor R922 keeps the open-circuit voltage at a safe level when the meter switch is in other positions.

When the transceiver is in the "receive" position and the meter switch is at ALC, the meter indicates the relative strength of the received signal in S units. The circuit operates just as it does when it measures ALC voltage except that the current in V3 is now controlled by the AVC voltage at the grid of V3.

The "meter-zero" control is adjusted for a zero indication on the meter with the antenna disconnected and RF gain control at the full clockwise position. The decrease in plate current (due to a larger AVC voltage) that occurs when a signal is received by V3 then appears as an indication on the S meter.

## TEST INSTRUMENTS

Test instruments of every description are used in TV-radio service shops, manufacturing labs, and even automobile repair garages. Among the most popular are oscilloscopes, volt-ohmmeters (VOM), signal generators, tube testers, etc. Obviously, we cannot cover all of these instruments here; however, we will discuss the schematic diagrams of two popular type test instruments, a field-effect VOM and a color bar signal generator.

### VOM

The field-effect VOM is a relatively new test instrument and its rather quick acceptance is attributed to the fact that is combines the portability of a VOM with the advantages of the VTVM (vacuum tube voltmeter). Primarily, the unit is battery-operated and since it uses field-effect transistors the high input impedance equals that obtainable only with a VTVM.

The schematic diagram of an FET-VOM is shown in Fig. 8-6. It uses a balanced differential amplifier circuit, formed by field-effect transistors TR1 and TR2, for resistance (ohms) and DC voltage measurements. The test probes are connected to the two terminals marked positive and negative. When no input voltage is applied to TR1, ZERO ADJ control R31 is set so that the voltages developed across R14 and R22 are equal. In other words, when the voltages are balanced, no current flows and the meter (M1) reads zero. DC BAL control R29 is an internal adjustment that is also used to zero the meter, but its purpose is to compensate for component aging.

Depending on the position of range switch S1A, the voltage to be measured is applied through one of the precision resistors to the base of TR1. The applied voltage upsets the bal-between TR1 and TR2, which in turn causes a current flow through the meter. The meter will then indicate the degree of unbalance in direct proportion to the input voltage and it can be read directly in terms of volts. There are seven DC and AC ranges provided by input divider network R1 through R8. Capacitors C2 through C8 compensate the divider network for AC voltages.

DC CAL control R15 is another internal adjustment used to calibrate the meter when a known DC voltage is applied. The circuit is also protected against overload from high voltage. If a high input voltage is applied and the switch is set in the wrong position (too low a range), diode CR1 will conduct and keep the voltage applied to TR1 at a safe level, thus preventing damage to the transistor.

Resistance (ohms) measurements are made by forming a voltage divider with the unknown resistor. Referring to the schematic, there are five resistance ranges. In the R X 1 position, R9 is the known value. In the R x 10 position, R10 is the known value. The voltage then developed across the known resistor in the divider network is read on the meter in terms of "ohms." Before any resistance measurement is made, the meter is adjusted to fullscale by shorting the test leads together. This applies the full voltage from battery B1 to

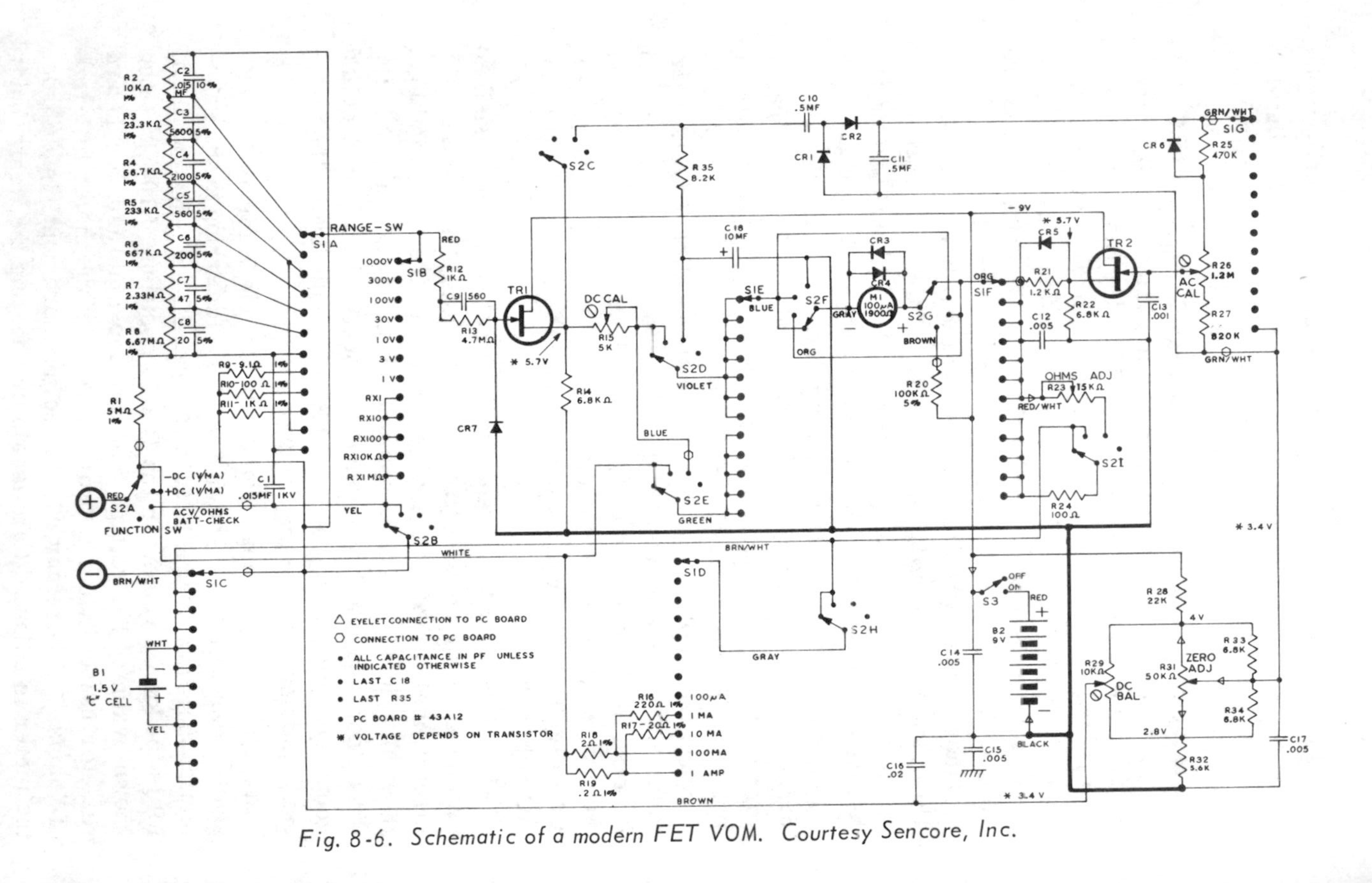


Fig. 8-6. Schematic of a modern FET VOM. Courtesy Sencore, Inc.

the input of TR1. Then OHMS ADJ control R23 is re-set to give a full-scale meter reading. Now, when the external resistor (unknown) is connected between the test leads, the meter reading will indicate proportionately lower.

When AC voltages are to be measured, the input is applied to TR1 through the same divider netwrok used for DC measurements—R2 through R8. However, the output of TR1 is fed to a peak-to-peak detector consisting of C10, C11, CR1, and CR2. From the detector a DC voltage is applied to TR2 through another divider consisting of R25, R26, R27, and CR6. The meter is in the source circuit of TR2. The DC voltage developed in this source circuit is, therefore, indicated on the meter in direct proportion to the peak-to-peak AC voltage applied to TR1. Diodes CR5 and CR6 are used to compensate for temperature changes so that meter readings remain accurate over a wide range of temperature.

When a DC current measurement is made, the input is connected through the meter and shunt resistors R16 through R19. The transistors and associated circuitry are not used. On the 100 microamp range, the meter is connected directly to the test lead inputs.

Diodes CR3 and CR4 are used to protect the meter movement itself from any excessive overload up to several amps. The diodes in turn are protected by R24 which will burn up when the maximum current rating of the diodes is exceeded.

### Color-Bar Generator

A color-bar generator is actually a miniature transmitter that operates on the lower VHF-TV channels. It produces black-and-white and color test signals used for set-up adjustments and troubleshooting.

Referring to Fig. 8-7 (foldout Panel P), the heart of this generator is a 189-kHz crystal-controlled oscillator, TR1. A signal from the oscillator is used to gate the color signal after first shaping it to the necessary waveform in stages TR2 and TR8. These signals form the dots and vertical lines by going through the differentiating circuit of C19, R26, and dot gate, CR3. The signals are also used to trigger the first counter stage, TR3.

This generator uses three counter stages—TR3, TR4, and

TR7. They are identical, except for the components which determine their respective operating frequencies. They are essentially blocking oscillators with timing components in the emitter circuits. The first counter (TR3) is triggered by the 189-kHz oscillator signal and it divides this frequency by 12, thus producing the horizontal line frequency of 15,750 Hz. The output of TR3 is used to develop horizontal sync pulses in TR12 and also to trigger the next counter stage, TR4.

TR4 divides the 15,750-Hz signal alternately by 17 and 18, as controlled by the bistable multivibrator (MV) TR5 and TR6, through R14. The output of the MV provides one source of pulses at 450 Hz through C14 to the thrid counter stage, TR7. A second source of pulses, also at 450 Hz, is fed to TR7 through C15 from the half-line MV, TR10 and TR11. However, this second source of pulses occurs midway between the first source of pulses so that when they are "mixed" in TR7 they appear in the output as a single source of 900-Hz pulses. The third counting stage, TR7, then divides this 900 Hz frequency by 15 to produce the 60-Hz vertical frequency. The output from TR7 is used to develop vertical sync pulses in TR12.

The half-line MV fires each time TR4 divides by 17 and generates a new pulse 20 to 40 microseconds later as controlled by the INTERLACE control, R36. Since TR7 locks to this source of pulses (from C15) every other time it fires (it divides by an odd number), one field (as viewed on a TV raster) can be shifted with respect to the other field plus or minus approximately 10 microseconds.

Output signals from the collectors of bistable MV TR5 and TR6 are mixed together to form horizontal line pulses in TR9. Since the bistable MV switches (turns on and off) each time TR4 fires, the horizontal line pulses are generated at the same rate. In other words, they are spaced alternately by 17 and 18 horizontal lines. Thus, they always begin at the start of the horizontal sync pulse. The width of the horizontal line pulse is determined by R30, C21, and C22.

Signals from color oscillator TR13 are gated or triggered at a 189-kHz rate through CR4 from the 189-kHz oscillator. These signals appear across COLOR OUTPUT control R51 when function switch S1 is in the color-bar position. When S1 is in any other position, the supply voltage is removed from the color oscillator and shaper TR8 to prevent spurious operation.

Color signals from R51, vertical line or dot signals from CR3, and horizontal line signals from TR9 are selected individually or in combination by S1, depending on the desired pattern. The signal (or signals) are then "mixed" with the composite sync signal from TR12 across CR5, R57, and R58. C35 and R53 are used to help isolate the signal sources from the composite sync signal. CR5 clips the negative-going sync signal so that the sync amplitude across R57 and R58 is approximately at the same level as the positive signal at this point.

RF oscillator TR14 is tunable from 55 to 84 MHz (Channels 2-6) by C39. The output from the collector is amplitude modulated by the composite video signal in modulator diode CR6. This modulated RF is then coupled through C41 to the RF output cable which is terminated to match the 300-ohm antenna terminals on the TV set. The 12-volt DC power for this test instrument is supplied by batteries and feeds all stages except the master oscillator, TR1, the shaper, TR2, and the three counter stages, TR3, TR4, and TR7. The supply voltage to these stages is regulated at 8 volts by zener diode CR1.

## SPECIALIZED EQUIPMENT

There are hundreds of electronic devices which could be categorized as "special." You would have to include garage door openers, burglar alarms, or fire-detection systems. To give you an idea of what some of these units look like schematically, we will discuss a smoke detector and a home protection system.

### Smoke Detector System

The schematic in Fig. 8-8 (foldout Panel Q) is a transistorized smoke-detection and heat-sensor unit designed for homes and offices. It uses very little power and so is designed to operate all the time. It is a sending unit and a remote receiver which receives its signal through the AC power line.

### Transmitter

The schematic and the block diagram in Fig. 8-9 can be used to follow the circuit. As shown, the unit uses an encapsu-

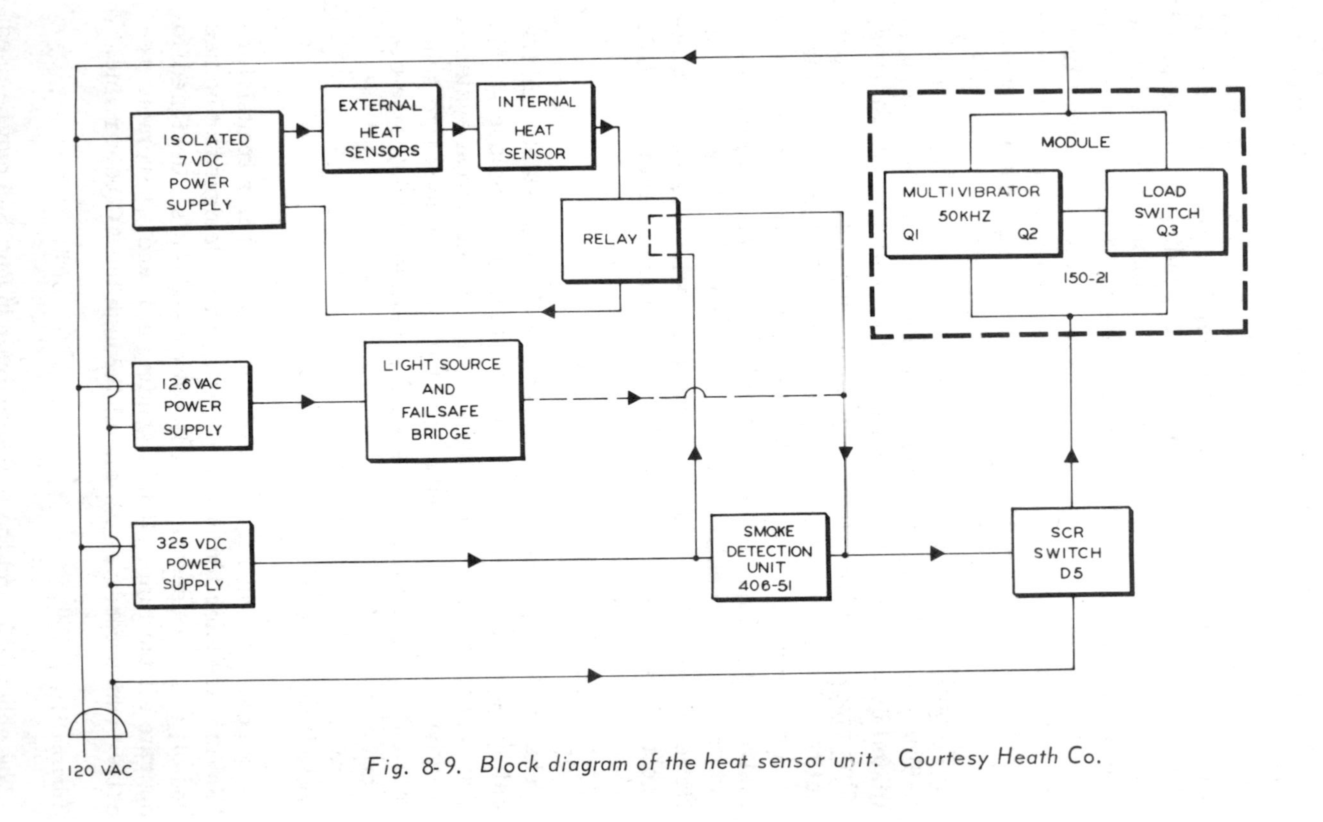


*Fig. 8-9. Block diagram of the heat sensor unit. Courtesy Heath Co.*

lated or modular circuit operating as a 50-kHz transmitter. The transmitter module consists of Q101, Q102, and switching transistor Q103. The 50-kHz multivibrator frequency is determined by R103, R104, C101, C102, and frequency trimmer C5. The frequency trimmer is used to make minor adjustments of the transmitter frequency. The 50-kHz signal from the transmitter is coupled from the collector of Q102 to the base of Q103 by C103 and R106. Resistor R107 acts as a voltage divider to protect the base of Q103 from a voltage overload.

The signal from Q102 turns Q103 on and off at a 50-kHz rate. When the transmitter is switched on Q103 acts like a short circuit between its emitter and collector. This places R8 and C104 across the power line and they act as a load for the transistor. Transistor Q103 switches at a 50-kHz rate only on the positive half cycles of the AC line voltage. Since this on-off action puts R8 and C104 across the power line, the power line current flow is also changed at a 50-kHz rate. The changing current then develops a 50-kHz signal voltage that is pulse-modulated by the 60-Hz line voltage. A 50-kHz modulated signal is thus transmitted through the power line to the companion receiver.

## Smoke Detector

The smoke-detection part of this unit consists of an LDR (light-dependent resistor), a half-wave power supply, the sensitivity control, and the gate circuit of an SCR (silicon controlled rectifier), D5. The halfwave power supply consists of D3, D4, C2, and C3 to supply 325v DC to the sensitivity control, R5.

The sensitivity control sets the amount of voltage across the LDR, which is mounted inside the smoke detection unit assembly. The LDR resistance is normally one to three megohms. However, when smoke enters the smoke detection unit, light
R6 is a current-limiting resistor used to protect the SCR gate from damage. The current through R7 sets up a voltage across the resistor which is applied to the gate of the SCR.
is reflected from the smoke onto the LDR, causing it to decrease in resistance. The more smoke, the lower the resistance goes. As the resistance of the LDR decreases, the current increases through the series circuit of the LDR, R6 and R7.

When the SCR gate voltage reaches .7 volts DC, the SCR conducts and applies a pulsating DC voltage across the transmitter module, causing a 50-kHz signal to be transmitted. Capacitor C4 bypasses any AC voltages which may be present at the SCR gate.

The 12.6-volt secondary winding of T1 provides the supply voltage for the smoke detector lamp circuit. Lamp PL-1 is connected in an AC bridge circuit with R1, R2, R3, R7, and D2.

The bridge circuit has two balanced legs. One leg consists of the smoke detector lamp PL-1 and R2; the other leg consists of R1 and R3. As long as these two legs remain balanced only a small current is present. If the smoke detector lamp burns out or is removed from the socket, the bridge balance is upset. This causes a current flow in the circuit from point E in the bridge, through R1, D2, and R7, then back through point F and R2. As current flows through R7, the resulting voltage drop is applied to the gate of the SCR. When the SCR gate voltage reaches .7 volts DC, the SCR conducts. As before, this applies a pulsating DC voltage to the transmitter module and causes a 50-kHz signal to be transmitted.

Zener diodes D6 and D7 are connected across the smoke detector lamp for voltage regulation. The diodes limit changes in the smoke detection lamp brilliance during changing line voltage conditions.

#### Heat Sensor

The 6.3-volt secondary of transformer T1 provides the supply voltage for the heat-sensor circuit. The supply voltage is rectified by D1 and filtered by capacitor C1. Relay current flows from the transformer through D1, the auxiliary input terminal strip (a jumper wire or external heat sensors), heat sensor TS1, through relay coil RLY1, back to the transformer.

The current flow through RLY1 energizes the relay and opens contacts 2 and 4. When heat sensor TS1 (or an external heat sensor) senses a temperature rise, it breaks the current path to the relay, causing it to de-emergize or open. When the relay opens, contacts 2 and 4 close, applying 325 volts DC across voltage-divider resistors R6, R7, and R9. When the voltage across R7 reaches .7 volts DC, the SCR will conduct and again cause the transmitter to operate.

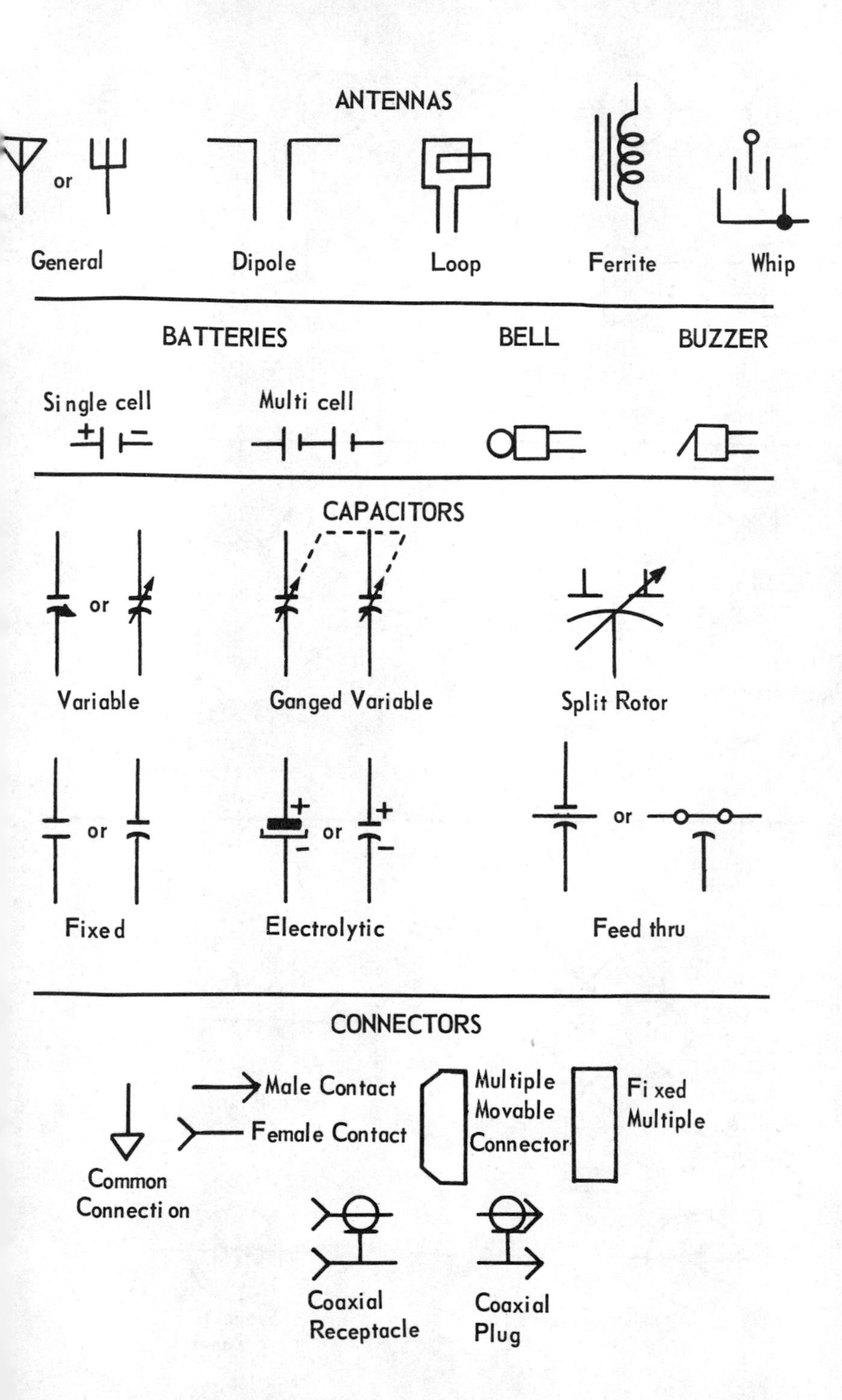
ANTENNAS
or
General
Dipole
Loop
Ferrite
Whip
BATTERIES
BELL
BUZZER
Single cell
+
Multi cell
CAPACITORS
or
Variable
Ganged Variable
Split Rotor
or
Fixed
+
-
or
+
-
Electrolytic
or
Feed thru
CONNECTORS
Male Contact
Female Contact
Multiple
Movable
Connector
Fixed
Multiple
Common
Connection
Coaxial
Receptacle
Coaxial
Plug

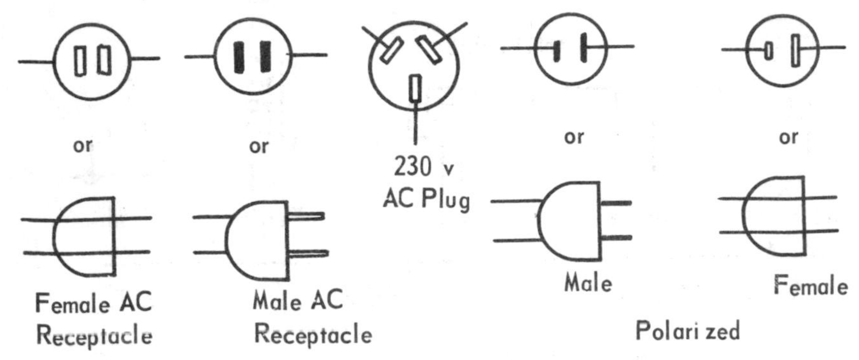


## CRYSTALS

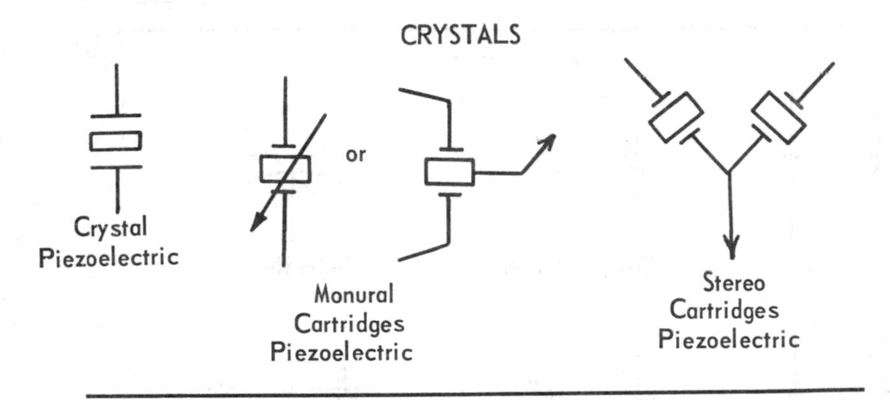


## DIODES

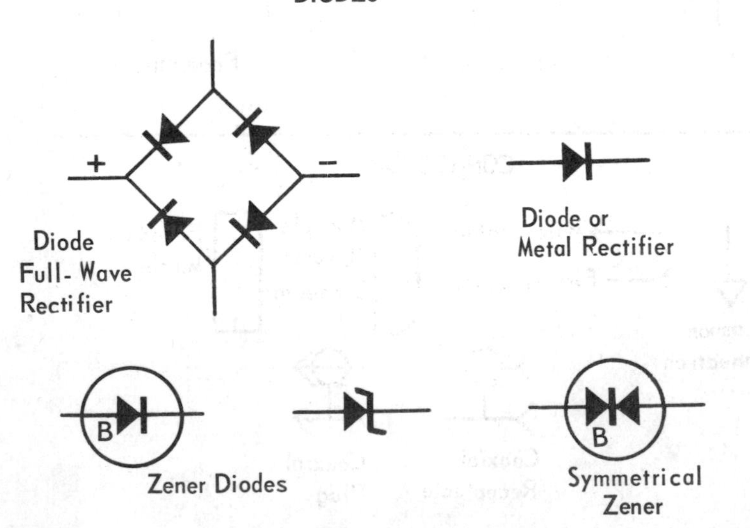

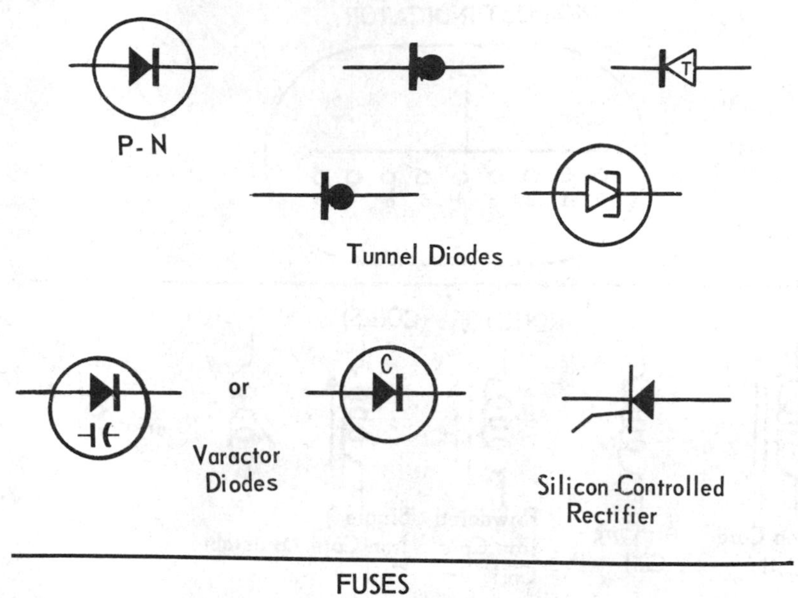


## FUSES

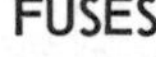

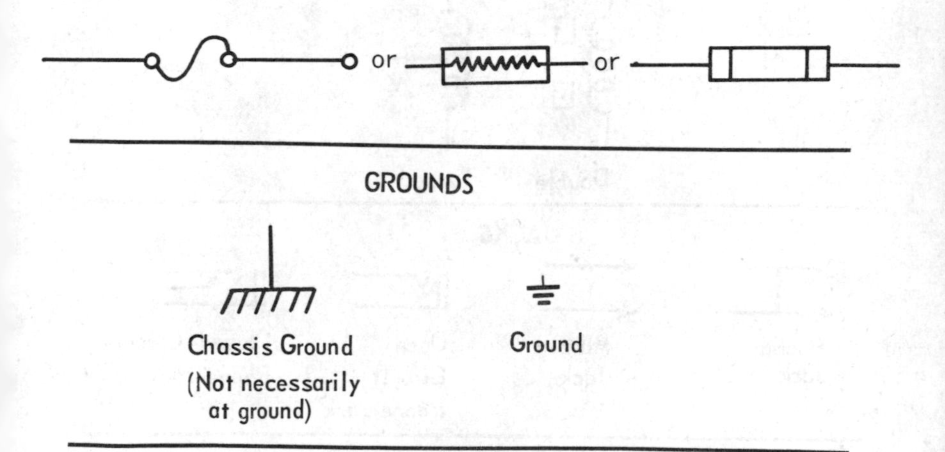


## HEADPHONES

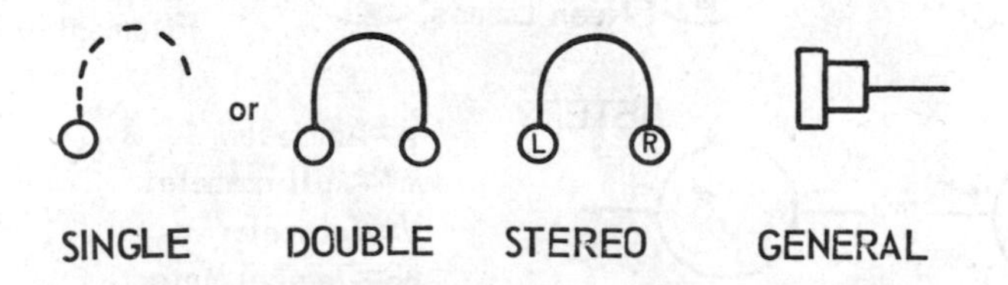

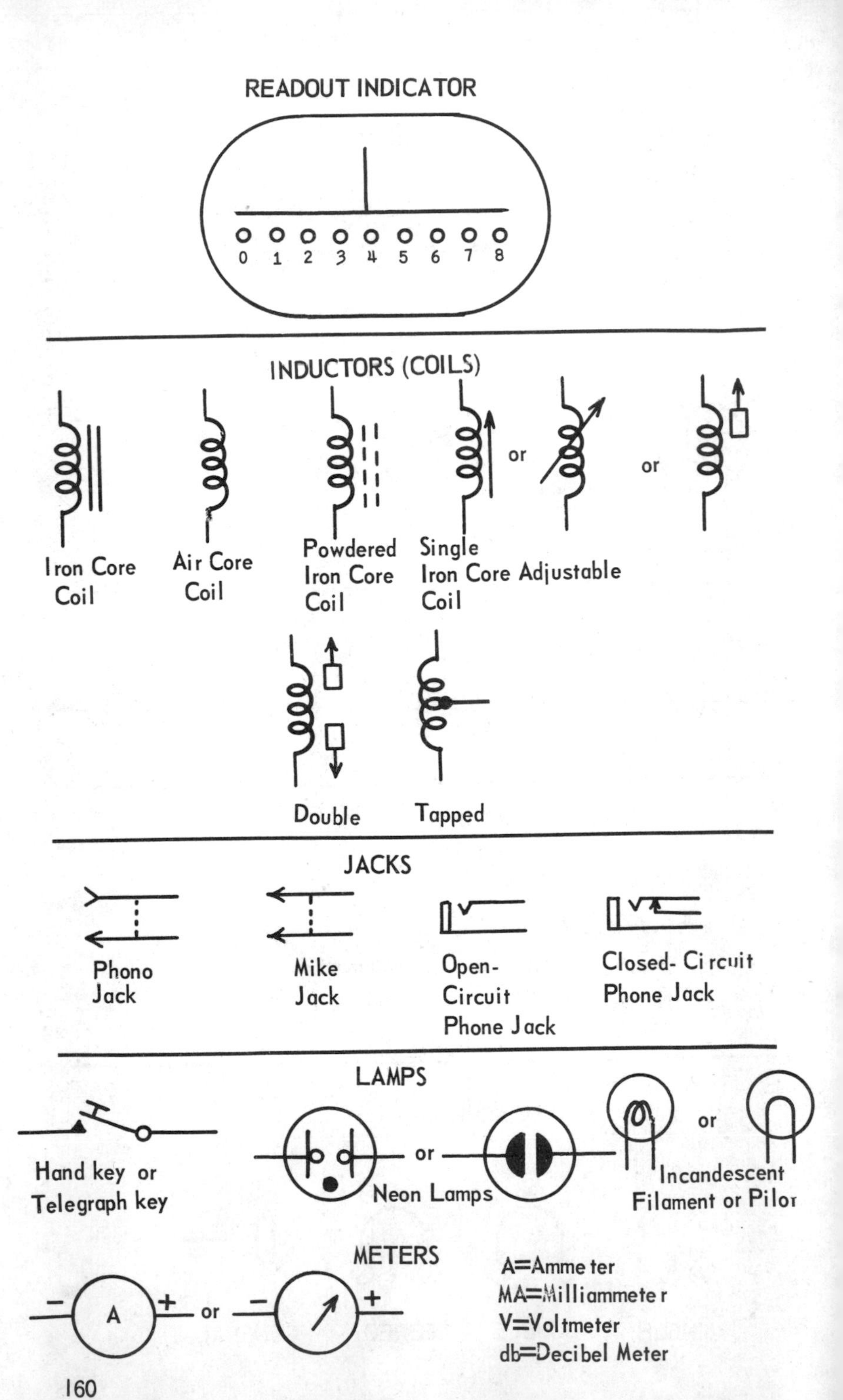

READOUT INDICATOR
0 1 2 3 4 5 6 7 8
INDUCTORS (COILS)
or
or
Iron Core Coil
Air Core Coil
Powdered Iron Core Coil
Single Iron Core Adjustable Coil
Double
Tapped
JACKS
Phono Jack
Mike Jack
Open-Circuit Phone Jack
Closed-Circuit Phone Jack
LAMPS
Hand key or Telegraph key
or
Neon Lamps
or
Incandescent Filament or Pilot
METERS
A
or
A=Ammeter
MA=Milliammeter
V=Voltmeter
db=Decibel Meter

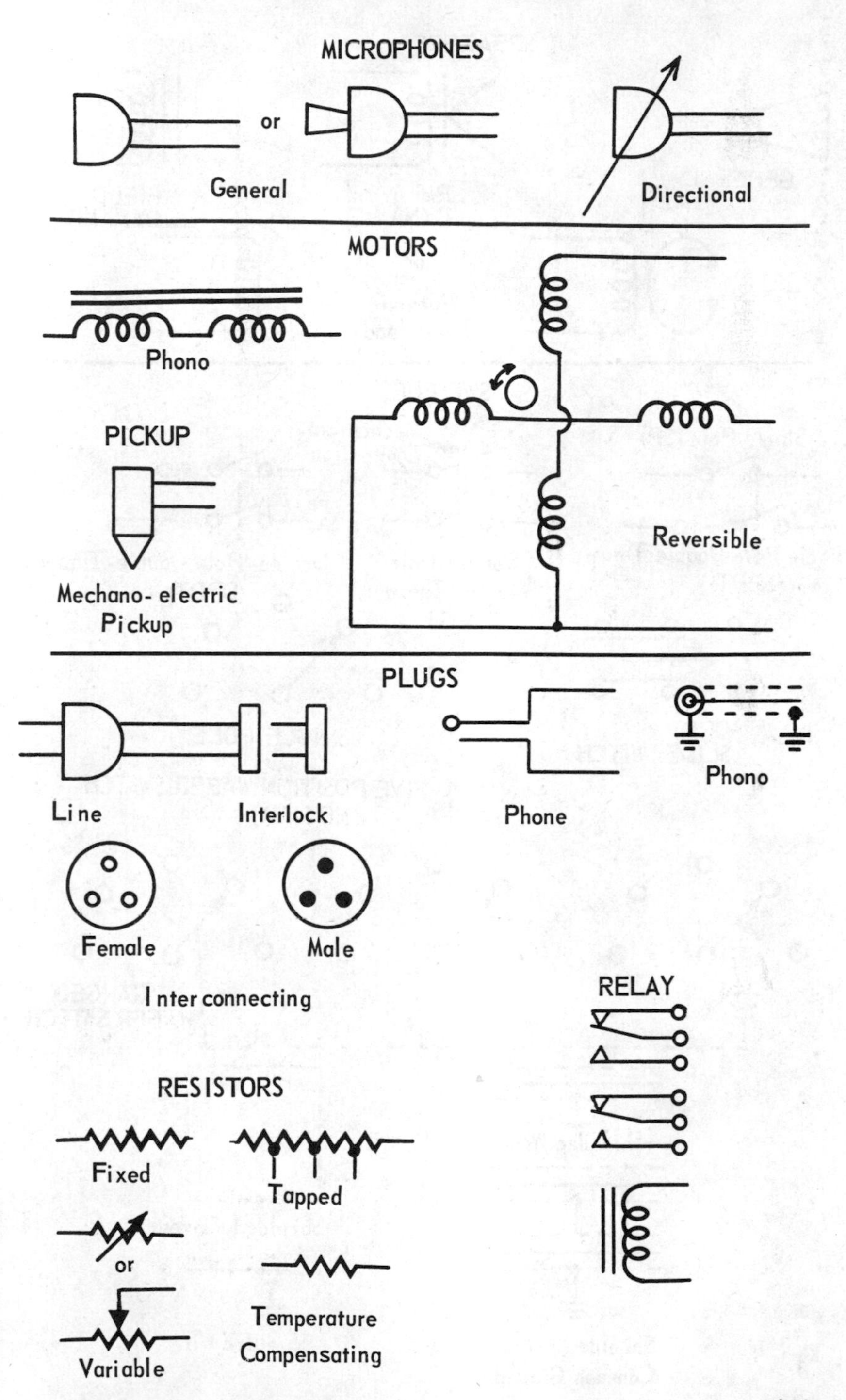
MICROPHONES
or
General
Directional
MOTORS
Phono
PICKUP
Mechano- electric
Pickup
Reversible
PLUGS
Line
Interlock
Phone
Phono
Female
Male
Inter connecting
RELAY
RESISTORS
Fixed
Tapped
or
Variable
Temperature
Compensating

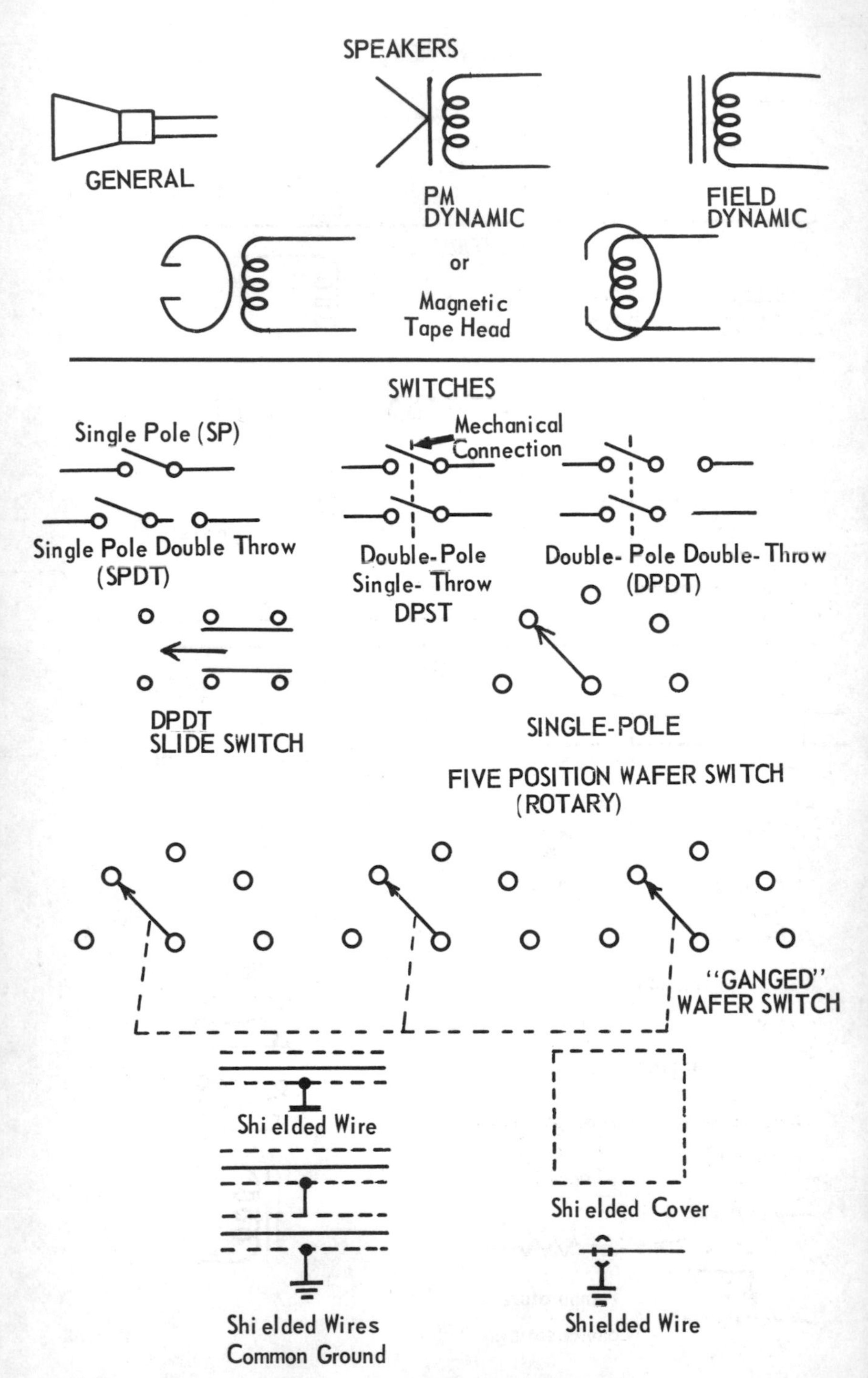
SPEAKERS
GENERAL
PM
DYNAMIC
FIELD
DYNAMIC
or
Magnetic
Tape Head
SWITCHES
Single Pole (SP)
Mechanical
Connection
Single Pole Double Throw
(SPDT)
Double-Pole
Single- Throw
DPST
Double- Pole Double- Throw
(DPDT)
DPDT
SLIDE SWITCH
SINGLE-POLE
FIVE POSITION WAFER SWITCH
(ROTARY)
"GANGED"
WAFER SWITCH
Shielded Wire
Shielded Cover
Shielded Wires
Common Ground
Shielded Wire

TRANSFORMERS

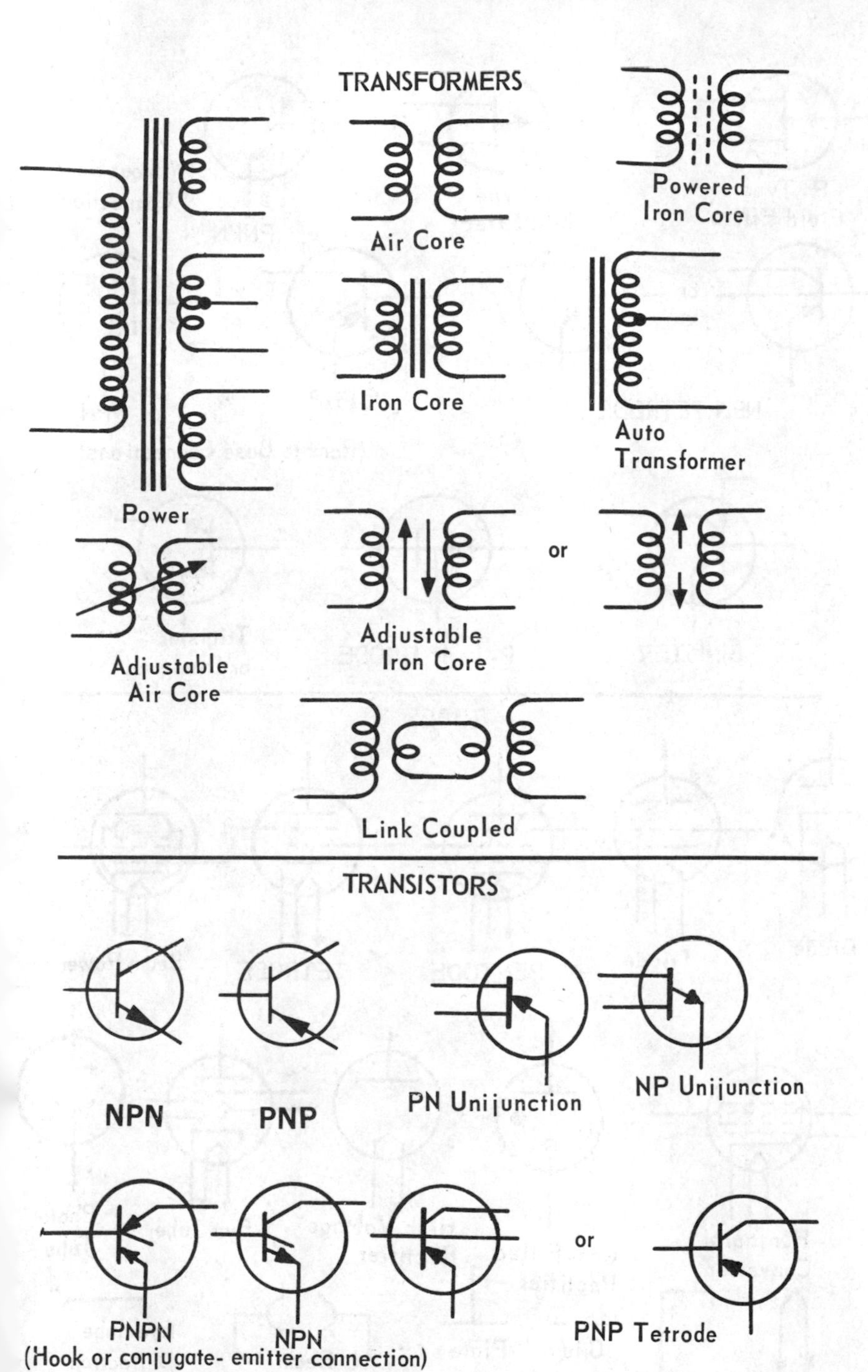

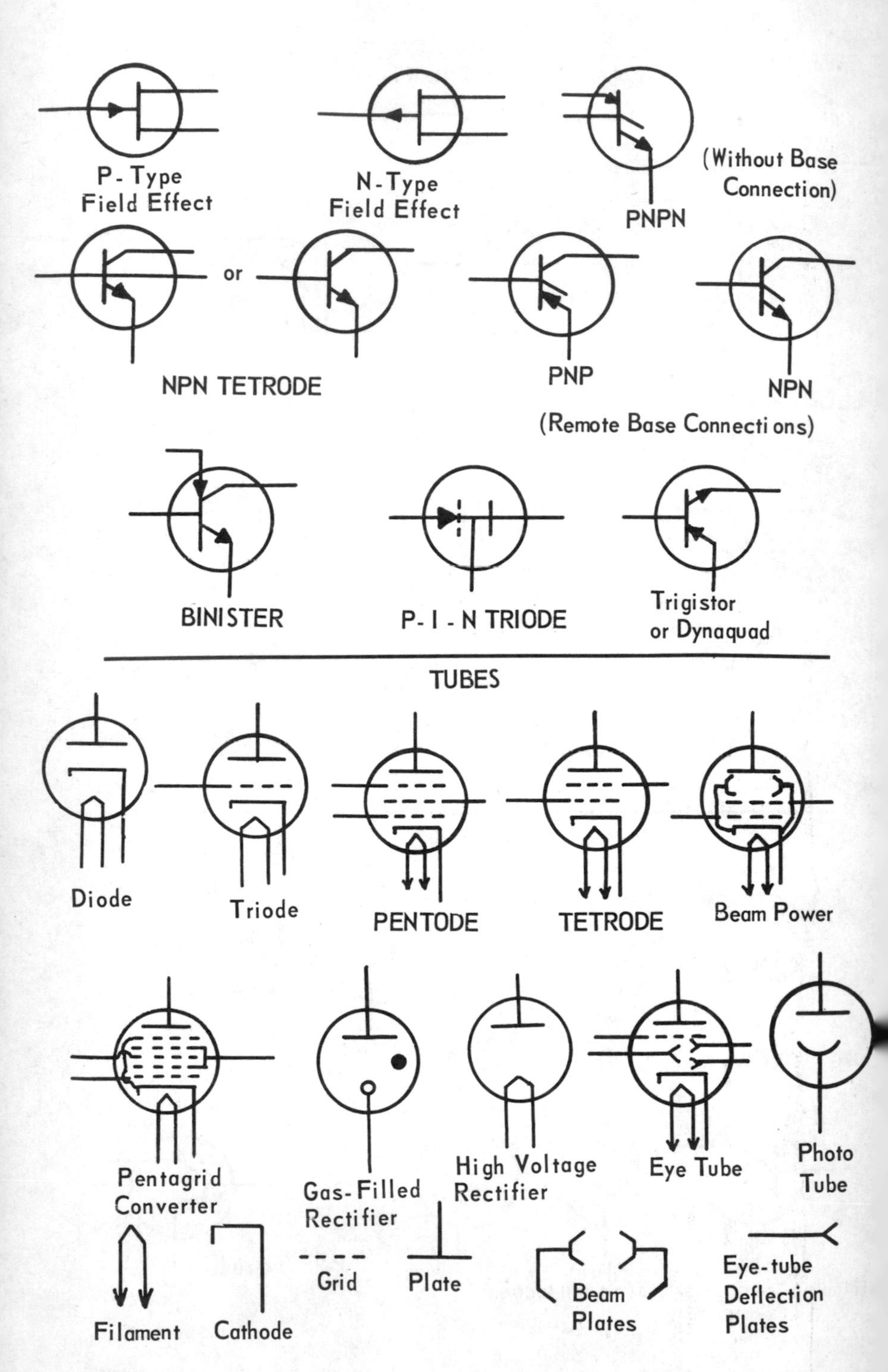

P-Type
Field Effect
N-Type
Field Effect
PNPN
(Without Base
Connection)
or
NPN TETRODE
PNP
NPN
(Remote Base Connections)
BINISTER
P-I-N TRIODE
Trigistor
or Dynaquad
TUBES
Diode
Triode
PENTODE
TETRODE
Beam Power
Pentagrid
Converter
Gas-Filled
Rectifier
High Voltage
Rectifier
Eye Tube
Photo
Tube
Filament
Cathode
Grid
Plate
Beam
Plates
Eye-tube
Deflection
Plates

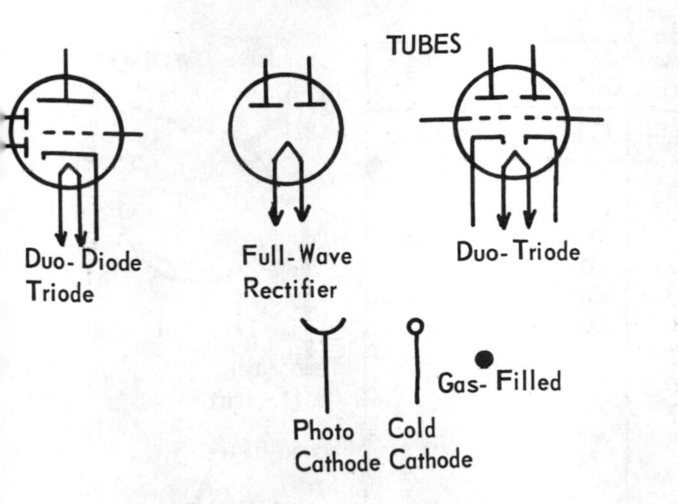
TUBES
Duo-Diode Triode
Full-Wave Rectifier
Duo-Triode
Two-Section Triode
Photo Cathode
Cold Cathode
Gas-Filled

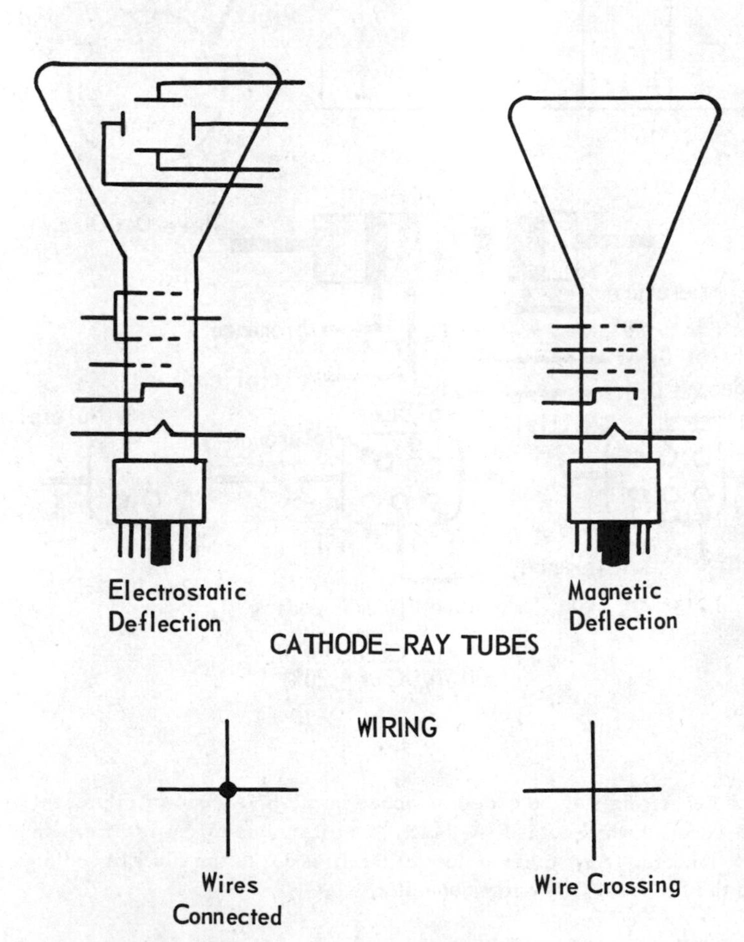
Electrostatic Deflection
Magnetic Deflection
CATHODE–RAY TUBES
WIRING
Wires Connected
Wire Crossing

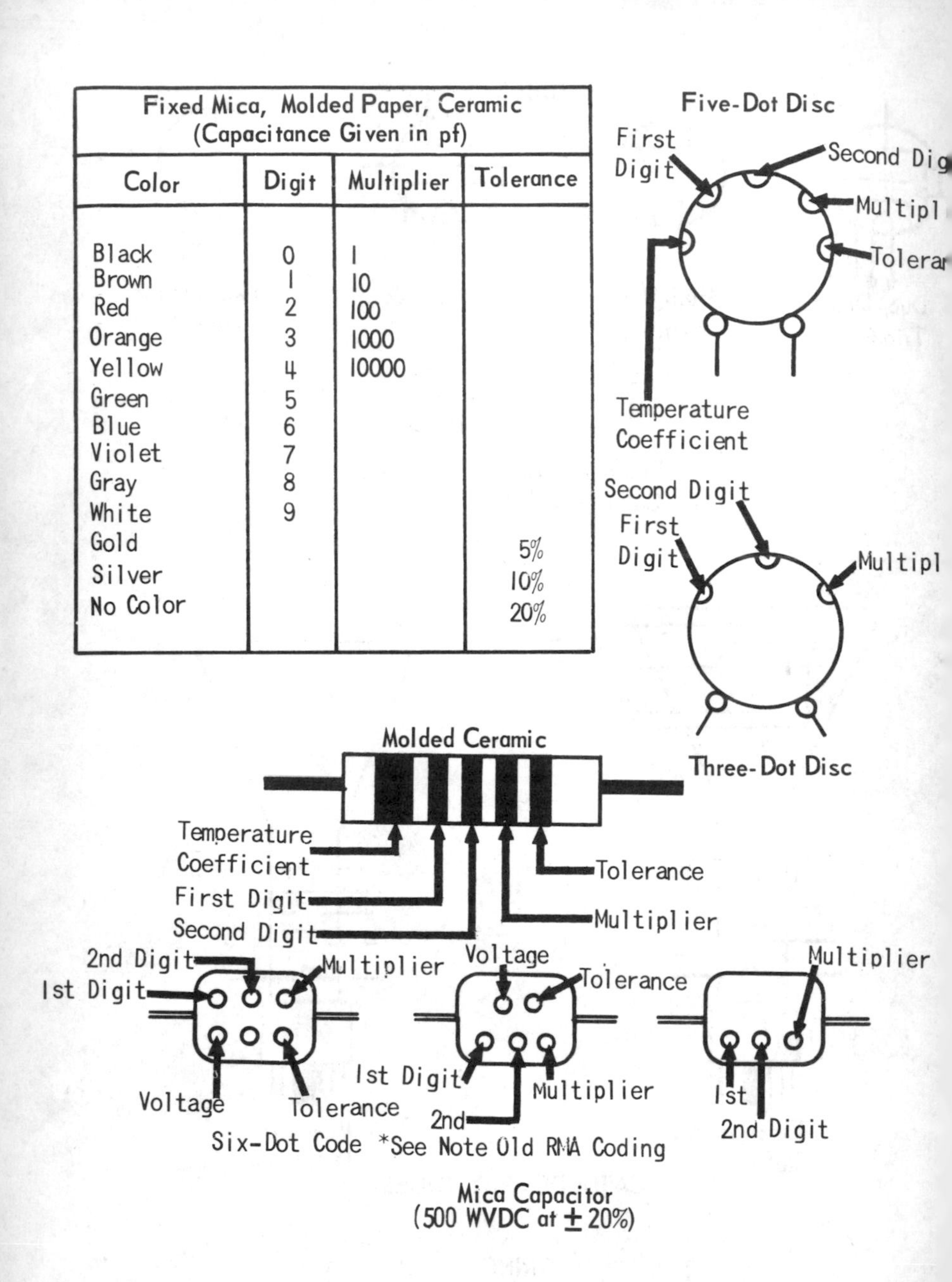

| Fixed Mica, Molded Paper, Ceramic (Capacitance Given in pf) | | | |
|---|---|---|---|
| Color | Digit | Multiplier | Tolerance |
| Black | 0 | 1 | |
| Brown | 1 | 10 | |
| Red | 2 | 100 | |
| Orange | 3 | 1000 | |
| Yellow | 4 | 10000 | |
| Green | 5 | | |
| Blue | 6 | | |
| Violet | 7 | | |
| Gray | 8 | | |
| White | 9 | | |
| Gold | | | 5% |
| Silver | | | 10% |
| No Color | | | 20% |



Mica Capacitor
(500 WVDC at ± 20%)

*Note
Mica capacitors may be coded as above in old RMA code or in present EIA code. A white dot is EIA, black is military and silver is American War standard. Any other color for the first dot is the old EIA coding and the first four dots show capacitor value.

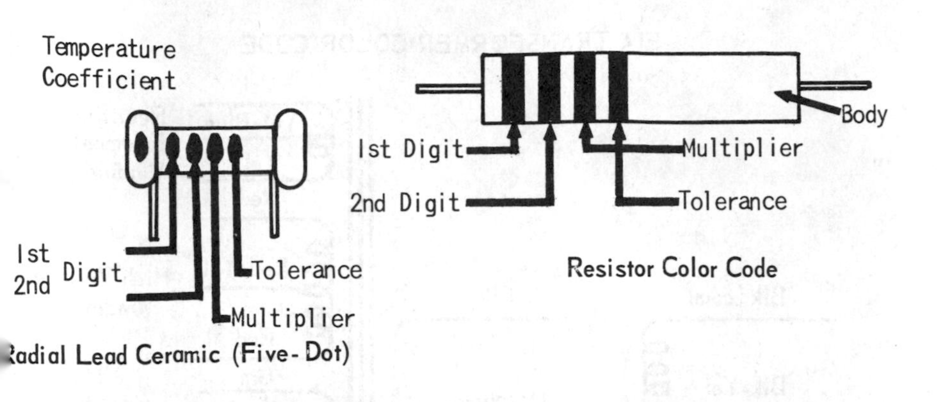


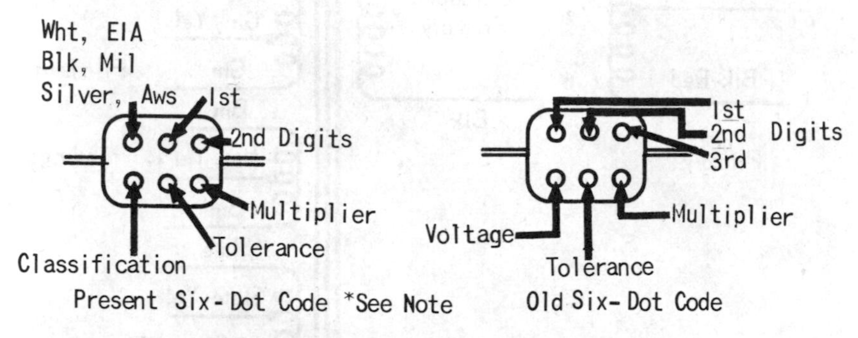


| EIA Color Code | | | |
|---|---|---|---|
| **Color** | **Digit** | **Multiplier** | **Tolerance** |
| Black | 0 | | |
| Brown | 1 | 0 | |
| Red | 2 | 00 | |
| Orange | 3 | 000 | |
| Yellow | 4 | 0000 | |
| Green | 5 | 00000 | |
| Blue | 6 | 000000 | |
| Violet | 7 | | |
| Gray | 8 | | |
| White | 9 | | |
| Gold | | 0.1 | ±5% |
| Silver | | 0.01 | ±10% |
| No Band | | | ±20% |

# EIA TRANSFORMER COLOR CODE

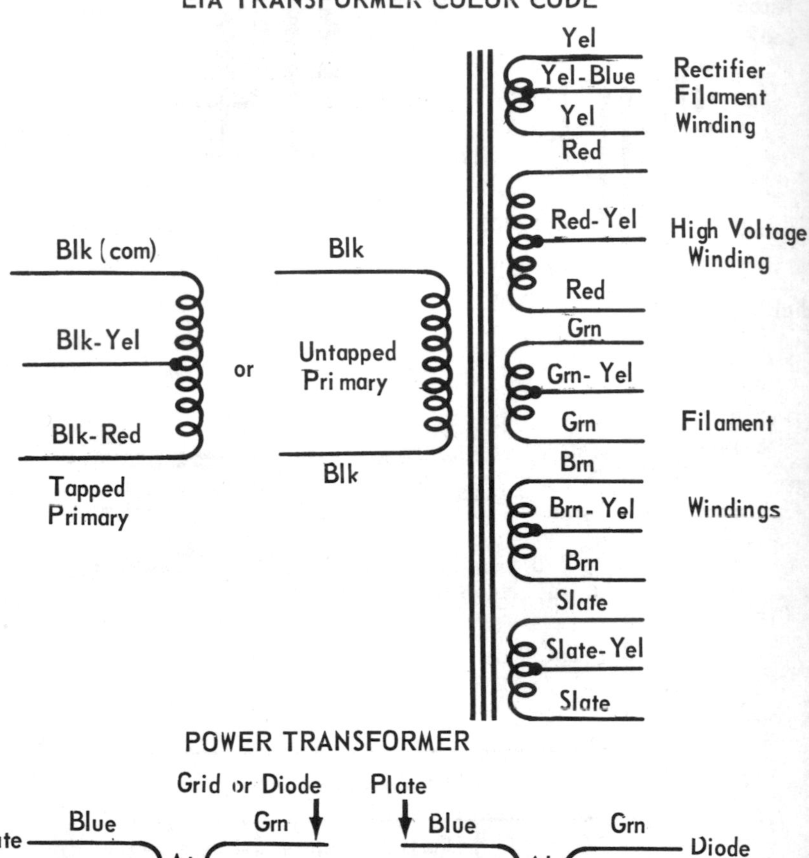


POWER TRANSFORMER

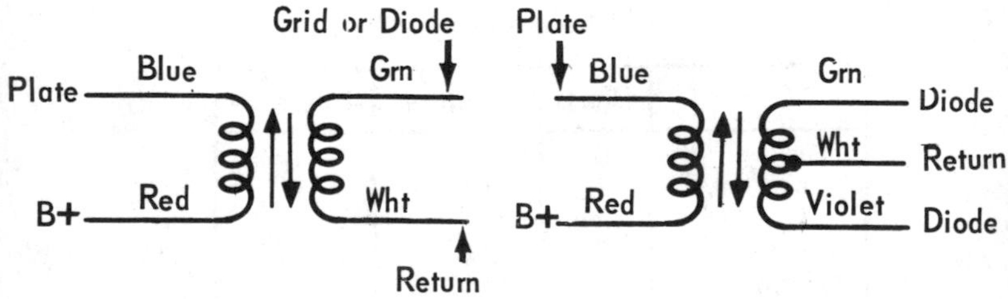


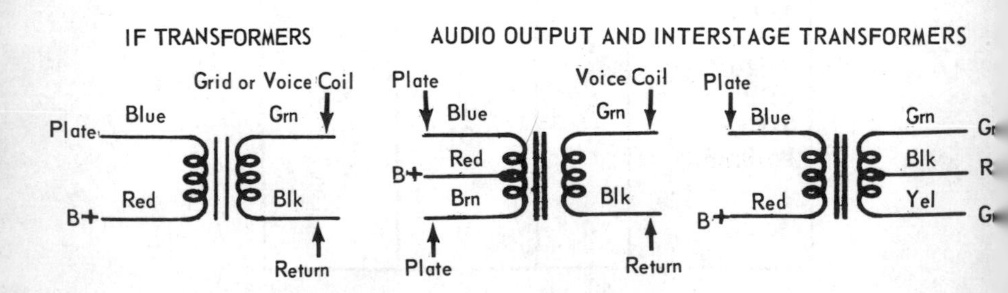

## ELECTRONIC AND ELECTRICAL ABBREVIATIONS

| TERM | ABBREVIATION |
|---|---|
| adjustable | adj |
| alternating current | AC |
| ambient | amb |
| ampere | a |
| ampere-hour | ah |
| amplitude modulation | AM |
| antilogarithm | antilog |
| approximate, -ly | approx |
| atmosphere | atm |
| atto-($10^{-18}$) | a |
| audio frequency | AF |
| automatic frequency control | AFC |
| automatic gain control | AGC |
| automatic volume control | AVC |
| average | avg |
| beat-frequency oscillator | BFO |
| bel | b |
| binary coded decimal | BCD |
| bits per second | b/s |
| British thermal unit | BTU |
| broadcast | bc |
| calibrate, calibration | cal |
| calorie | cal |
| cathode-ray oscilloscope | CRO |
| cathode-ray tube | CRT |
| centi ($10^{-2}$) | c |
| centigram | cg |
| centimeter | cm |
| centimeter-gram-second | cgs |
| circular mil | cmil |
| clockwise, continuous wave | CW |
| cosecant | csc |
| cosine | cos |
| cotangent | cot |
| coulomb | C |
| counterclockwise | CCW |
| cubic centimeter | $cm^3$ |

| TERM | ABBREVIATION |
|---|---|
| cubic foot | $ft^3$ |
| cubic foot per minute | $ft^3/min$ |
| cubic foot per second | $ft^3/s$ |
| cubic inch | $in.^3$ |
| cubic meter | $m^3$ |
| cubic meter per second | $m^3/s$ |
| cycle per second | c/s |
| deka-(10) | da |
| deci-($10^{-1}$) | d |
| decibel | db |
| decibel referred to 1 milliwatt | dbm |
| decibel referred to 1 watt | dbw |
| decibel referred to 1 volt | dbv |
| degree Celsius | $^oC$ |
| degree Fahrenheit | $^oF$ |
| degree Kelvin | $^oK$ |
| diameter | dia |
| digital voltmeter | DVM |
| diode-transistor logic | DTL |
| direct current | DC |
| direct-current working volts | dcwv |
| double-pole, double-throw | DPDT |
| double-pole, single-throw | DPST |
| electromotive force | emf |
| electronvolt | ev |
| equation | eq. |
| external | ext |
| farad | f |
| field-effect transistor | FET |
| Figure | Fig. |
| filament | fil |
| foot | ft |
| foot per second | ft/s |
| foot poundal | ft-pdl |
| foot-pound force | ft-lbf |
| foot-second | ft-s |
| frequency | freq |
| frequency modulation | FM |
| gauss | g |

| TERM | ABBREVIATION |
|---|---|
| giga-($10^9$) | G |
| gigacycles per second | Gc/s |
| gigaelectron volt | gev |
| gigahertz | GHz |
| gilbert | gb |
| gram | g |
| gravity | g |
| ground | gnd |
| hecto-($10^2$) | h |
| henry | h |
| hertz | Hz |
| high frequency | HF |
| horsepower | hp |
| hour | h |
| inch | in. |
| inch per second | in./s |
| infrared | IR |
| inside diameter | ID |
| insulated-gate field-effect transistor | IGFET |
| integrated circuit | IC |
| intermediate frequency | IF |
| kilo-($10^3$) | k |
| kilocycle per second | kc/s |
| kilogram | kg |
| kilohertz | kHz |
| kilohm | K |
| kilometer | km |
| kilovar | kvar |
| kilovolt | KV |
| kilovoltampere | KVA |
| kilowatt | KW |
| kilowatt-hour | KWH |
| lambert | L |
| logarithm | log |
| low frequency | LF |
| maximum | max |
| maxwell | mx |
| mega-($10^6$) | m |
| megacycle per second | mc/s |
| megahertz | MHz |

| TERM | ABBREVIATION |
|---|---|
| megavolt | mv |
| megawatt | mw |
| megohm | m |
| Metal-oxide semiconductor | MOS |
| metal-oxide semiconductor field-effect transistor | MOSFET |
| meter | m |
| micro-($10^{-6}$) | mu |
| microampere | ua |
| microfarad | mfd (sometimes uf) |
| microhenry | uh |
| microhm | uΩ |
| micrometer, micron | um |
| micromho | umho |
| microsecond | us |
| microvolt | uv |
| microwatt | uw |
| milli-($10^{-3}$) | m |
| milliampere | ma |
| millibar | mbar |
| milligram | mg |
| millihenry | mh |
| millimeter | mm |
| millimho | mmho |
| millimicron | (see nanometer) |
| milliohm | mΩ |
| millisecond | ms |
| millivolt | mv |
| milliwatt | mw |
| minimum, minute | min |
| nano-($10^{-9}$) | n |
| nanoampere | na |
| nanofarad | nf |
| nanohenry | nh |
| nanometer | nm |
| nanosecond | ns |
| nanowatt | nw |
| negative | neg |
| negative-positive-negative | NPN |
| newton | N |

| TERM | ABBREVATION |
|---|---|
| normally-closed | NC |
| normally-open | NO |
| number | No. |
| oersted | oe |
| ohm | Ω |
| ounce | oz |
| outside diameter | OD |
| part per million | ppm |
| peak | pk |
| peak inverse voltage | PIV |
| peak-to-peak | pk-pk |
| pico-($10^{-12}$) | p |
| picoampere | pa |
| picofarad | pfd |
| picosecond | ps |
| picowatt | pw |
| positive | pos |
| positive-negative-positive | PNP |
| potentiometer | pot |
| pound | lb |
| pound per square foot | lb/ft$^2$ |
| pound per square inch | lb/in.$^2$ |
| power factor | PF |
| pulse-amplitude modulation | PAM |
| pulse-code modulation | PCM |
| pulse-duration modulation | PDM |
| pulse-position modulation | PPM |
| pulse repetition frequency | PRF |
| pulse-width modulation | PWM |
| radian | rad |
| radio frequency | RF |
| reactive voltampere | (see var) |
| receiver | rcvr |
| reference | ref |
| root-mean-square | rms |
| secant | sec |
| second | s |
| sensitivity | sens |
| siemens | S |
| silicon controlled rectifier | SCR |

| TERM | ABBREVIATION |
|---|---|
| sine | sin |
| single-pole double-throw | SPDT |
| single-pole single-throw | SPST |
| single sideband | SSB |
| square | sq |
| square foot | $ft.^2$ |
| square inch | $in.^2$ |
| square meter | $m^2$ |
| standard | std |
| standing-wave ratio | SWR |
| steradian | sr |
| synchronous, synchronizing | sync |
| tangent | tan |
| television | TV |
| temperature | temp |
| tera-($10^{12}$) | T |
| teracycle per second | Tc/s |
| terahertz | THz |
| telsa | T |
| transistor-transistor logic | TTL |
| transistor voltmeter | TVM |
| transmit-receive | T-R |
| traveling-wave tube | TWT |
| ultra-high frequency | UHF |
| ultraviolet | UV |
| vacuum-tube voltmeter | VTVM |
| var (reactive voltampere) | var |
| variable-frequency oscillator | VFO |
| versus | vs |
| very high frequency | VHF |
| very low frequency | VLF |
| volt | v |
| voltage standing-wave ratio | VSWR |
| voltampere | VA |
| watt | W |
| watthour | WH |
| weber | wb |

## WIRE SIZES

| AWG B & S Gauge | Enamel | Double Covered Cotton D.C.C. | Single Covered Cotton S.C.C. | Diameter (inches) | Current Carrying Capacity @700 CM Per Amp | Ohms Per 1,000 Ft. @20°C |
|---|---|---|---|---|---|---|
| 0000 | -- | -- | -- | .4600 | 302.3 | 0.04901 |
| 000 | -- | -- | -- | .4096 | 239.7 | 0.06180 |
| 00 | -- | -- | -- | .3648 | 190.1 | 0.07793 |
| 0 | -- | -- | -- | .3249 | 150.7 | 0.09827 |
| 1 | -- | 3.3 | 3.3 | .2893 | 119.6 | 0.1239 |
| 2 | -- | 3.6 | 3.8 | .2576 | 94.8 | 0.1563 |
| 3 | -- | 4.0 | 4.2 | .2294 | 75.2 | 0.1970 |
| 4 | -- | 4.5 | 4.7 | .2043 | 59.6 | 0.2485 |
| 5 | -- | 5.0 | 5.2 | .1819 | 47.3 | 0.3133 |
| 6 | -- | 5.6 | 5.9 | .1620 | 37.5 | 0.3951 |

| | | | | | | |
|---|---|---|---|---|---|---|
| 7 | -- | 6.2 | 6.5 | .1443 | 29.7 | 0.4982 |
| 8 | 7.6 | 7.1 | 7.4 | .1285 | 23.6 | 0.6282 |
| 9 | 8.6 | 7.8 | 8.2 | .1144 | 18.7 | 0.7921 |
| 10 | 9.6 | 8.9 | 9.3 | .1019 | 14.8 | 0.9989 |
| 11 | 10.7 | 9.8 | 10.3 | .09074 | 11.8 | 1.260 |
| 12 | 12.0 | 10.9 | 11.5 | .08081 | 9.33 | 1.588 |
| 13 | 13.5 | 12.0 | 12.8 | .07196 | 7.40 | 2.003 |
| 14 | 15.0 | 13.8 | 14.2 | .06408 | 5.87 | 2.525 |
| 15 | 16.8 | 14.7 | 15.8 | .05707 | 4.65 | 3.184 |
| 16 | 18.9 | 16.4 | 17.9 | .05082 | 3.69 | 4.016 |
| 17 | 21.2 | 18.1 | 19.9 | .04526 | 2.93 | 5.064 |
| 18 | 23.6 | 19.8 | 22.0 | .04030 | 2.32 | 6.385 |
| 19 | 26.4 | 21.8 | 24.4 | .03589 | 1.84 | 8.051 |
| 20 | 29.4 | 23.8 | 27.0 | .03196 | 1.46 | 10.15 |
| 21 | 33.1 | 26.0 | 29.8 | .02846 | 1.16 | 12.80 |
| 22 | 37.0 | 30.0 | 34.1 | .02535 | .918 | 16.14 |
| 23 | 41.3 | 31.6 | 37.6 | .02257 | .728 | 20.36 |
| 24 | 46.3 | 35.6 | 41.5 | .02010 | .577 | 25.67 |
| 25 | 51.7 | 38.6 | 45.6 | .01790 | .458 | 32.37 |
| 26 | 58.0 | 41.8 | 50.2 | .01594 | .363 | 40.81 |

| | | | | | | |
|---|---|---|---|---|---|---|
| 27 | 64.9 | 45.0 | 55.0 | .01420 | .288 | 51.47 |
| 28 | 72.7 | 48.5 | 60.2 | .01264 | .228 | 64.90 |
| 29 | 81.6 | 51.8 | 65.4 | .01126 | .181 | 81.83 |
| 30 | 90.5 | 55.5 | 71.5 | .01003 | .144 | 103.2 |
| 31 | 101.0 | 59.2 | 77.5 | .008928 | .114 | 130.1 |
| 32 | 113.0 | 62.6 | 83.6 | .007950 | .090 | 164.1 |
| 33 | 127.0 | 66.3 | 90.3 | .007080 | .072 | 206.9 |
| 34 | 143.0 | 70.0 | 97.0 | .006305 | .057 | 260.9 |
| 35 | 158.0 | 73.5 | 104.0 | .005615 | .045 | 329.0 |
| 36 | 175.0 | 77.0 | 111.0 | .005000 | .036 | 414.8 |
| 37 | 198.0 | 80.3 | 118.0 | .004453 | .028 | 523.1 |
| 38 | 224.0 | 83.6 | 126.0 | .003965 | .022 | 659.6 |
| 39 | 248.0 | 86.6 | 133.0 | .003531 | .018 | 831.8 |
| 40 | 282.0 | 89.7 | 140.0 | .003145 | .014 | 1,049.0 |

## GLOSSARY OF TERMS

A battery—The battery used to supply electron tube filaments in battery-operated devices.
AC—Abbreviation for alternating current.
AGC—Automatic gain control. The circuit samples demodulated gain levels and provides an automatic correction bias which maintains a predetermined signal amplitude.
Air core—The term used to describe inductors having no magnetic core material.
Align—To tune or adjust a circuit to meet specific requirements.
Alternating current—Current which has periodic alternations of positive and negative polarities.
Alternator—A device which produces alternating current.
Ammeter—An instrument that measures the rate of current flow.
Ampere—A unit of current.
Amplification—The process of increasing the current, voltage, or power of a signal.
Amplification factor—An indication of the general amplification characteristics of a vacuum tube, defined as the ratio of the change in plate voltage to a small change in the grid voltage, with the plate current remaining at a constant level. The symbol for amplification factor is the Greek letter u.
Amplifier—A device designed to increase the signal voltage, current, or other waveform measured in either a positive or negative direction.
Amplitude Modulation—The type of modulation commonly used for "standard" radio broadcasting. The "carrier" signal is modulated by low-frequency audio signals so that the overall waveform amplitude varies above and below the normal carrier level at a rate and amplitude change corresponding to the modulating signal.
Anode—The plate or positive electrode.
Antenna—A device used for receiving or transmitting RF signals. Sometimes called an aerial.
Aquadag—The graphite coating in a cathode-ray or television tube.
Attenuate—To diminish the amplitude of a signal.

Attenuator—A device for reducing signal amplitude by using either fixed or variable components.
Audio amplification—The increase of signal amplitude within the audible frequency range.
Autotransformer—A single-coil transformer where primary and secondary are connected together in one winding.
AVC—Automatic volume control.
Average value—The average of all instantaneous values of I or E in one half cycle. The product of 0.636 times the peak amplitude.
B battery—The battery used for supplying anode potentials in battery-operated devices.
Bandpass filter—An electronic network which passes a specific band of frequencies.
Base terminal—The electrode of a transistor usually compared to the grid of a vacuum tube.
Beta—The current gain in a grounded-emitter transistor amplifier. The symbol for current gain is the Greek letter B.
BFO—Beat-frequency oscillator.
Bias—The difference of potential applied between the grid and cathode of a tube or between transistor elements to provide an operating point at zero signal input.
Blanking—Electron-beam cut-off in a cathode-ray tube during beam retrace time.
Bleeder—One or more resistors shunting the output of a power supply to improve voltage regulation by providing a fixed current drain.
Broadcast band—The term generally applied to the RF frequency span between 550 kHz and 1600 kHz allocated to "standard" radio transmission.
Buffer stage—An amplifier or other circuit usually employed in RF amplifier (transmitter) stages to isolate the oscillator and subsequent amplifiers.
Bus bar—A primary power distribution point connected to the main power source.
C battery—The battery used for supplying grid-bias in battery-operated circuits.
Capacitance—The quantity of electric charge (usually in fractional farad quantities) which a capacitor is capable of "storing" a given voltage.
Capacitive reactance—The opposition which a capacitor offers to AC at a specific signal frequency.

Capacitor—A device capable of "storing" electrons between two conducting surfaces insulated by a dielectric.
Carrier—An RF signal capable of being modulated to carry information.
Cascade—Circuits or stages connected in sequence.
Cathode—The element in a vacuum tube which emits electrons.
Cathode follower—A tube circuit where the output signal appears across the cathode with the anode at signal ground. Also a grounded-collector transistor circuit.
Cathode-ray tube—A tube with a phosphor-treated face on which an electron beam traces an image.
Center frequency—The term usually applied to the unmodulated FM carrier frequency.
Characteristic impedance—The impedance of a transmission line or attenuator network.
Charge—The quantity of energy stored by a capacitor or storage-type battery.
Choke coil—An inductor designed to provide a high impedance to AC.
Chopper—A circuit which converts DC to AC by periodic interruption (chopping) of the DC.
Circuit breaker—An electromagnetic or thermal device that opens a circuit when the current exceeds a certain value.
Clamper—A circuit designed to restore the DC component of a signal waveform.
Class A amplifier—An amplifier biased to operate on the linear portion of the characteristic curve.
Class B amplifier—An amplifier biased to operate at or near the tube or transistor cut-off point. Positive alternations of the input signal cause current flow.
Class C amplifier—An amplifier biased beyond the cut-off point so current flows for only a portion of the positive alternations of the input signal.
Clipper—A circuit designed to remove portions of the input signal amplitude.
Coaxial cable—A transmission line consisting of two concentric conductors insulated from each other.
Cold-cathode tube—A tube which requires no external heat current source to produce electron emission.
Color codes—The identification of electronic components by color bands or dots which relate to numerical values.

Colpitts oscillator—An oscillator using series capacitors across the resonant circuit inductor.
Condenser—See Capacitor.
Conductance—The current-carrying ability of a wire. The unit value is mho and is the reciprocal of resistance.
Conductor—A medium which carries a flow of electric current.
Continuous wave—An unmodulated RF waveform of constant amplitude. Usually the term applied to a wave transmitted in bursts of short and long duration to form the Morse code.
Control grid—The grid to which a signal is usually applied in a tube.
Conventional current flow—The theory that current flows from positive to negative.
Converter—The stage in a superheterodyne receiver which produces the IF signal by mixing the RF carrier with a locally-generated signal.
Counter EMF—Counter electromotive force; an emf induced in a coil or armature in opposition to the applied voltage.
Counting circuit—A circuit which produces a voltage in proportion to the frequency of uniform input pulses.
Coupling—The effective "linkage" connecting two electronic circuits; usually transformers, capacitors, and inductors.
CRO—Cathode-ray oscilloscope.
Cross-modulation—Modulation of a desired signal by an unwanted signal.
Crossover frequency—The frequency in a multiple-speaker where the signal is divided and fed to high- and low-frequency systems.
Crystal oscillator—A signal-generating circuit in which the frequency is controlled by a piezo-quartz crystal.
Current limiter—A fuse-like protective device designed to limit current flow in a circuit.
Cut-off frequency—The frequency of a filter or other circuit beyond which signal flow ceases.
CW—See Continuous waves.
Cycle—In AC, one complete alternation, positive and negative.
DC amplifier—An amplifier using direct coupling (no coupling capacitors or transformers).
DC restorer—A clamper circuit which restores the DC level to a signal waveform.

Decibel—One tenth of a bel.

Decoupling circuit—A resistance-capacitance circuit which isolates signal-carrying circuits from circuits common to other signal-carrying circuits.

De-emphasis circuit—An RC filter used after FM detector systems to decrease high-frequency signal levels which were increased during transmission.

Delayed AVC—An automatic volume-control circuit designed to produce an AVC bias only for signals above a fixed amplitude.

Demodulation—A signal-rectifying system which extracts the modulating-signal component from the modulated carrier.

Detection—To separate modulation from the signal.

Deviation ratio—The ratio of maximum FM carrier deviation to the highest frequency audio-modulating signal employed.

Dielectric—The insulating material between the two conductors, such as in a capacitor, or the insulating material between transmission line conductors.

Diode—A two-element tube or two-terminal solid-state rectifier.

Direct current—Current flow in one direction.

Discriminator—The "detector" used in frequency modulation. It is used also to compare two AC signals.

Distortion—Unwanted modification of a desired signal.

Doubler—A circuit in transmitting systems which doubles the frequency of the input signal. In power supply systems, a circuit for doubling voltage amplitude.

Driver stage—An audio or RF amplifier stage preceding the final or power amplifier.

Eddy currents—Stray induced currents in a conducting material caused by a varying magnetic field.

Effective value—The value of alternating current or voltage equal to the product of 0.707 times the peak amplitude.

Efficiency—The ratio of output power to input power, generally expressed as a percentage.

Electrode—A terminal used to emit, collect, or control electrons.

Electrolyte—A solution or a substance which is capable of conducting electricity; it may be in the form of either a liquid or a paste.

Electrolytic capacitor—A capacitor utilizing an electrolyte to form the dielectric insulation.

Electromagnet—A magnet made by passing current through a coil of wire wound on a soft iron core.

Electromotive force (EMF)—The force that produces a current in a circuit (voltage).

Electronic switch—A circuit which introduces a start-stop action by electronic means.

Emitter—Transistor electrode similar, functionally, to the cathode of a tube.

Farad—The unit of capacitance. Fractional values are used in practical electronics (mfd, pfd).

Feedback—A transfer of energy from the output of a circuit back to its input.

Feedback oscillator—A signal-generating circuit which employs regenerative feedback to sustain oscillations.

Ferrite—A metallic compound used for high-Q core materials in inductors.

Filament—The electrode in a vacuum tube which is heated for electron emission or which transfers its heat to a separate cathode.

Filter—A circuit designed to pass certain signal components and attenuate others.

Filter capacitor—An electrolytic capacitor used in power supplies to reduce ripple.

Filter choke—An inductor used in power supplies to reduce ripple.

Flip-flop—A bistable circuit which can be triggered to its other state by an input signal or pulse.

Forward bias—The bias applied between the base and emitter of a transistor.

Frequency—The number of complete cycles per second in an alternating wave. A cycle includes negative and positive "excursions."

Frequency division—A circuit designed to reduce the repetition rate of pulse waveforms or decrease the frequency of AC signals.

Frequency modulation—A system where the frequency of the carrier signal is shifted above and below its normal "center" frequency by the modulating signal.

Full-wave rectifier—A power supply circuit which uses both alternations of the AC waveform to produce direct current.

Gain—The ratio of the output signal to the input signal, voltage or current.

Galvanometer—An instrument used to measure small DC currents.

Gas tube—A tube containing gas which must ionize before conduction can occur.

Generator—A machine that changes mechanical energy into electrical energy by rotating coils of wire within a fixed magnetic field.

Grid—A wire, usually in the form of a spiral, used to control the electron flow in a vacuum tube.

Grounded base—A transistor amplifier circuit similar to a grounded-grid tube circuit.

Grounded collector—A transistor circuit similar to a cathode-follower tube circuit.

Grounded emitter—A transistor circuit similar to the conventional grounded-cathode tube amplifier.

Grounded grid—A tube circuit with the control grid at signal ground.

Half-wave rectifier—A tube or solid-state diode which converts AC to pulsating DC by rectifying one alternation of each AC cycle.

Harmonic—A signal related to a fundamental signal by some multiple.

Heater—A vacuum-tube electrode which heats the cathode.

Henry—The basic unit of inductance. One henry represents the amount of inductance present when a current change of 1 amp per sec produces an induced voltage of 1v.

Heptode—A tube with seven electrodes.

Heterodyne—The electronic mixing of two signals of different frequencies to produce a third signal.

Hexode—A tube with six electrodes.

High fidelity—An audio system which reproduces the full audio-frequency spectrum with negligible distortion.

High-pass filter—A circuit that transfers high-frequency signals while attenuating the lows.

Hole—In semiconductors the space left vacant in an atom by a departed electron. Holes "flow" in a direction opposite to that of electrons and bear a positive charge.

Hysteresis—The phenomenon present in magnetic materials where the flux density (B) lags the magnetizing force (H).

Impedance—A combination of resistance and reactance which opposes AC current flow.

Inductance—The property of a coil which opposes a change in current.

Induction—The process of inducing a potential or magnetization in another component by magnetic lines of force.

Inductive reactance—The opposition an inductor offers to AC for a given signal frequency. It is measured in ohms.

Inductor—A circuit element designed so that inductance is its most important property, such as a coil.

In phase—The condition that exists when two AC waves of the same frequency pass through their maximum and minimum values of like polarity at the same instant in time.

Intermediate frequency—The signal obtained by heterodyning or mixing two signals of different frequencies.

Kilo—A prefix meaning 1,000.

Kilocycles (kc)—One thousand cycles. (The preferred unit now is kilohertz.)

Kirchhoff's Current Law—The basic law which states that the sum of currents flowing into any junction of an electric circuit is equal to the sum of currents flowing out of that junction.

Kirchhoff's Voltage Law—The basic law which states that the sum of voltage sources around any closed circuit is equal to the sum of the individual voltage drops across the resistances of the circuit.

Lag—The amount (in degrees) one AC wave is behind another in time.

Laminated core—A core built up from thin sheets of metal; used in transformers and relays.

Lead—The opposite of lag. Also, a connecting wire.

Level control—A variable control for adjusting signal levels.

Limiter—A circuit which limits the peak amplitudes of signal waveforms to a predetermined level.

Linear—A circuit where the output signal varies in direct proportion to the input.

Load—A resistor or transformer, usually, across which the output signal of a tube or transistor is developed.

Low-pass filter—A circuit designed to pass low-frequency signals and attenuate the highs.

Magnetic field—The area in which magnetic lines of force exist.

Megohm—A million ohms.

Mho—The unit of conductance, transconductance, or admittance; the word ohm spelled backwards.

Micro—A prefix meaning one-millionth.

Milliammeter—An ammeter constructed to measure fractional

(thousandths) values of an ampere.

Modulation—The process of modifying an RF carrier signal to transmit audio or video signal information over great distances.

Mutual inductance—The inductance (coupling) established when two coils are close together.

Null—Zero or minimum.

Octode—A tube with eight electrodes.

Ohm—The unit of resistance.

Ohmmeter—An instrument which measures resistance in ohms.

Ohm's Law—A basic law of electricity establishing the mathematical relationships between current, voltage, and resistance values (E equals IR).

Oscillator—A regenerative circuit designed to produce signals.

Oscilloscope—An instrument using a cathode-ray tube which presents a visual display of electric signals or waveforms.

Overmodulation—The modulation of an RF carrier in excess of 100%.

Pad—An attenuator circuit usually used as a coupling between circuits where the output of one is too high for the other.

Peak inverse voltage—The peak voltage a rectifier will handle without arcing internally with a polarity opposite to that causing conduction.

Peak-to-peak value—The over-all amplitude of a signal measured from its lowest (or most negative) peak to its highest (or most positive) peak.

Peak value—The instantaneous maximum value of a waveform or signal.

Pentagrid converter—A five-element tube used as a mixer-oscillator in superheterodyne receivers.

Phase angle—The angle of "lead" or "lag" between voltage and current in an AC waveform.

Plate resistance—The dynamic (AC signal) resistance of a tube.

Potentiometer—A variable resistor.

Power amplifier—An audio or RF amplifier designed to deliver signal energy (power) rather than signal voltage.

Power factor—The cosine of the phase angle between voltage and current; an efficiency rating.

Power supply—A circuit designed to furnish operating voltages and currents for electronic devices.

Preamplifier—An additional stage of amplification preceding another amplifier to increase signal amplitudes above a given level.

Push-pull circuit—Push-pull normally refers to an amplifier circuit with two tubes or transistors operating so that when one is conducting on a positive alternation, the other operates on a negative alternation.

Q—A symbol for the figure merit of an inductor.

Quiescent operating point—Zero-signal voltage and current.

Radio-frequency amplifier—An amplifier designed to increase RF signal levels.

Radio-frequency choke—An inductor designed to introduce reactance when used in series with a signal-carrying lead.

Ratio—The value obtained by dividing one number by another, indicating their relative proportional relationship.

Ratio detector—A dual-diode frequency-modulation "detector."

Reactance—The opposition to AC current flow offered by an inductor or capacitor.

Rectifier—A device that changes alternating current to unidirectional current.

Regulation—The degree by which voltage is held near its no-load value when a load is applied.

Relay—An electromechanical device used to remotely open or close a circuit.

Reluctance—The opposition offered by a material to magnetic lines of force.

Resistance—The opposition to current flow; measured in ohms.

Resonance—A condition in a tuned circuit where reactances cancel at a specific frequency.

Reverberation—Sound waves re-inforced by reflection.

Saturation—The point in a tube or transistor at which gain levels off despite further attempts to increase it.

Sawtooth voltage—A waveform characterized by a gradual rise and rapid decline of amplitude.

Screen grid—The electron-beam accelerating electrode in a tube.

Secondary emission—Electron emission from an electrode other than the cathode in a tube when struck by a high-velocity electron beam.

Self-bias—A circuit that produces bias within its associated circuits as a result of internal current flow.

Semiconductors—Solid-state devices of the transistor type.

Silicon-controlled rectifier—A solid-state rectifier in which conduction can be started by applying a control voltage.

Solenoid—An electromagnetic coil with a movable plunger.

Standing wave—Current and voltage waves on a transmission line formed by a reflection of the desired signal, caused by impedance mismatch.

Static—A fixed condition; no motion.

Stereophonic—Sound reproduction utilizing two or more amplification channels feeding respective loudspeaker systems.

Superheterodyne receiver—A radio or TV receiver employing a mixer stage to produce an intermediate frequency on all incoming signals; the IF is amplified by fixed-selectivity circuits.

Suppressor grid—A grid (usually between anode and screen grid) at ground potential to eliminate secondary emission.

Sweep generator—A signal generator whose output signal is varied (swept) through a given frequency range.

Tachometer—An instrument which indicates revolutions per minute.

Tank circuit—Usually refers to a parallel resonant circuit.

Tetrode—A four-electrode tube or transistor.

Thermionic emission—Production of electron emission by heat.

Thermistor—A resistor that changes its resistance value to compensate for temperature changes.

Thermocouple—A junction of two dissimilar metals that produces a voltage when heated.

Time constant—The product of R and C in a series circuit.

Trace—A visible line on the screen of a cathode-ray tube.

Transducer—A device for converting energy from one form to another, such as vibrations from a phonograph pickup into audible sounds.

Transformer—A device with two or more coils linked by magnetic lines of force; used to transfer energy from one circuit to another.

Transmission lines—Conductors used to carry energy from a source to a load.

Transient—An irregular signal of fractional duration as compared to the primary signal.

Transistor—A solid-state device.

Triggering—Starting an action in another circuit which then functions for a time under its own control.

Triode—A three-electrode vacuum tube with a cathode, control grid, and plate.

Tuned circuit—A circuit at resonance.

Turns ratio—The ratio of primary-to-secondary turns of a transformer.

Unmodulated—An RF carrier signal with no modulation.

Vacuum tube—An evacuated envelope containing two or more electrodes.

Vacuum-tube voltmeter—A high input impedance test instrument with a tube (or transistor) circuit.

Variable-frequency oscillator—A signal-generating circuit in which component values can be varied to alter the frequency of the output signal.

Vector—A line used to represent both direction and magnitude of AC signals.

Video amplifier—A circuit capable of amplifying a very wide range of frequencies, from the audio band and higher.

Volt—The unit of electrical potential (emf).

Voltage divider—Resistors placed in series across a voltage to obtain intermediate values of voltage.

Voltage doubler—A power-supply circuit so designed that the rectified voltage amplitude is almost double the input AC amplitude.

Watt—The unit of electric energy or power.

Waveform—The shape of the wave obtained when instantaneous values of an AC quantity are plotted against time in rectangular coordinates.

Wavelength—The distance, usually expressed in meters, traveled by a wave during the time interval of one complete cycle. It is equal to the velocity divided by the frequency.

Working voltage—The maximum voltage at which a device will operate continuously with safety.

Yagi antenna—An antenna system employing a basic antenna element as well as reflector and director rods.

Yoke—In a television receiver, a coil arrangement around the neck of the picture tube which provides electromagnetic deflection of the CRT beam vertically and horizontally.

Zener diode—A solid-state semiconductor that has voltage-regulation characteristics when subjected to reverse bias.

Zero bias—The absence of a potential between the grid and cathode of a tube, or between the emitter-base or other electrodes of a transistor.

# Index

## T



## U



## V



## W



## Y



## Z